THE LOG OF THE SUN

FRONTISPIECE BY
WALTER KING STONE

THE LOG
OF THE SUN

A Chronicle of Nature's Year

By WILLIAM BEEBE

GARDEN CITY PUBLISHING CO., INC.,
GARDEN CITY, NEW YORK

TO MY
Mother and Father
WHOSE ENCOURAGEMENT AND SYMPATHY
GAVE IMPETUS AND PURPOSE TO
A BOY'S LOVE OF NATURE

PREFACE

IN the fifty-two short essays of this volume I have presented familiar objects from unusual points of view. Bird's-eye glances and insect's-eye glances, at the nature of our woods and fields, will reveal beauties which are wholly invisible from the usual human view-point, five feet or more above the ground.

Who follows the lines must expect to find moods as varying as the seasons; to face storm and night and cold, and all other delights of what wildness still remains to us upon the earth.

Emphasis has been laid upon the weak points in our knowledge of things about us, and the principal desire of the author is to inspire enthusiasm in those whose eyes are just opening to the wild beauties of God's out-of-doors, to gather up and follow to the end some of these frayed-out threads of mystery.

Portions of the text have been published at various times in the pages of "Outing," "Recreation," "The Golden Age," "The New York Evening Post," and "The New York Tribune."

C. W. B.

TABLE OF CONTENTS

JULY

AUGUST

SEPTEMBER

OCTOBER

NOVEMBER

DECEMBER

A fiery mist and a planet,
  A crystal and a cell;
A jelly fish and a saurian,
  And the caves where the cave men dwell;
Then a sense of law and beauty
  And a face turned from the clod,
Some call it evolution,
  And others call it God.

                    W. H. CARRUTH.

JANUARY

BIRDS OF THE SNOW

NO fact of natural history is more interesting, or more significant of the poetry of evolution, than the distribution of birds over the entire surface of the world. They have overcome countless obstacles, and adapted themselves to all conditions. The last faltering glance which the Arctic explorer sends toward his coveted goal, ere he admits defeat, shows flocks of snow buntings active with warm life; the storm-tossed mariner in the midst of the sea, is followed, encircled, by the steady, tireless flight of the albatross; the fever-stricken wanderer in tropical jungles listens to the sweet notes of birds amid the stagnant pools; while the thirsty traveller in the desert is ever watched by the distant buzzards. Finally when the intrepid climber, at the risk of life and limb, has painfully made his way to the summit of the most lofty peak, far, far above him, in the blue expanse of thin air, he can distinguish the form of a majestic eagle or condor.

At the approach of winter the flowers and insects about us die, but most of the birds take wing and fly to a more temperate climate, while their place is filled with others which have spent the summer farther to the north. Thus without stirring from our doorway we may become acquainted with many species whose summer homes are hundreds of miles away.

No time is more propitious or advisable for the amateur bird lover to begin his studies than the first of the year. Bird life is now reduced to its simplest terms in numbers and species, and the absence of concealing foliage, together with the usual tameness of winter birds, makes identification an easy matter.

In January and the succeeding month we have with us birds which are called permanent residents, which do not leave us throughout the entire year; and, in addition, the winter visitors which have come to us from the far north.

In the uplands we may flush ruffed grouse from their snug retreats in the snow; while in the weedy fields, many a fairy trail shows where bob-white has passed, and often he will announce his own name from the top of a rail fence. The grouse at this season have a curious outgrowth of horny scales along each side of the toes, which, acting as a tiny snowshoe, enables them to walk on soft snow with little danger of sinking through.

Few of our winter birds can boast of bright colours; their garbs are chiefly grays and browns, but all have some mark or habit or note by which they can be at once named. For example, if you see a mouse hitching spirally up a tree-trunk, a closer look will show that it is a brown creeper, seeking tiny insects and their eggs in the crevices of the trunk. He looks like a small piece of the roughened bark which has suddenly become animated. His long tail props him up and his tiny feet never fail to find a foothold. Our winter birds go in flocks, and where we see a brown creeper we are almost sure to find other birds.

Nuthatches are those blue-backed, white or rufous breasted little climbers who spend their lives defying the law of gravity. They need no supporting tail, and have only the usual number of eight toes, but they traverse the bark, up or down, head often pointing toward the ground, as if their feet were small vacuum cups. Their note is an odd nasal *nyĕh! nyĕh!*

In winter some one species of bird usually predominates, most often, perhaps, it is the black-capped chickadee. They seem to fill every grove, and, if you take your stand in the woods, flock after flock will pass in succession. What good luck must have come to the chickadee race during the preceding summer? Was some one of their enemies stricken with a plague, or did they show more than usual care in the selecting of their nesting holes? Whatever it was, during such a year, it seems certain that scores more of chickadee babies manage to live to grow up than is usually the case. These little fluffs are, in their way, as remarkable acrobats as are the nuthatches, and it is a marvel how the very thin legs, with their tiny sliver of bone and thread of tendon, can hold the body of the bird in almost any position, while the vainly hidden clusters of insect eggs are pried into. Without ceasing a moment in their busy search for food, the fluffy feathered members of the flock call to each other, *"Chick-a-chick-a-dee-dee!"* but now and then the heart of some little fellow bubbles over, and he rests an instant, sending out a sweet, tender, high call, a *"Phœ-be!"* love note, which warms our ears in the frosty air and makes us feel a real affection for the brave little mites.

Our song sparrow is, like the poor, always with us, at least near the coast, but we think none the less of him for that, and besides, that fact is true in only one sense. A ripple in a stream may be seen day after day, and yet the water forming it is never the same, it is continually flowing onward. This is usually the case with song sparrows and with most other birds which are present summer and winter. The individual sparrows which flit from bush to bush, or slip in and out of the brush piles in January, have doubtless come from some point north of us, while the song sparrows of our summer walks are now miles to the southward. Few birds remain the entire year in the locality in which they breed, although the southward movement may be a very limited one. When birds migrate so short a distance, they are liable to be affected in colour and size by the temperature and dampness of their respective areas; and so we find that in North America there are as many as twenty-two races of song sparrows, to each of which has been given a scientific name. When you wish to speak of our northeastern song sparrow in the latest scientific way, you must say *Melospiza cinerea melodia,* which tells us that it is a melodious song finch, ashy or brown in colour.

Our winter sparrows are easy to identify. The song sparrow may, of course, be known by the streaks of black and brown upon his breast and sides, and by the blotch which these form in the centre of the breast. The tree sparrow, which comes to us from Hudson Bay and Labrador, lacks the stripes, but has the centre spot. This is one of our commonest field birds in winter, notwithstanding his name.

The most omnipresent and abundant of all our winter visitors from the north are the juncos, or snowbirds. Slate coloured above and white below, perfectly describes these birds, although their distinguishing mark, visible a long way off, is the white V in their tails, formed by several white outer feathers on each side. The sharp chirps of juncos are heard before the ice begins to form, and they stay with us all winter.

We have called the junco a snowbird, but this name should really be confined to a black and white bunting which comes south only with a midwinter's rush of snowflakes. Their warm little bodies nestle close to the white crystals, and they

seek cheerfully for the seeds which nature has
provided for them. Then a thaw comes, and they
disappear as silently and mysteriously as if they
had melted with the flakes; but doubtless they are
far to the northward, hanging on the outskirts of
the Arctic storms, and giving way only when every
particle of food is frozen tight, the ground covered deep with snow, and the panicled seed clusters locked in crystal frames of ice.

The feathers of these Arctic wanderers are
perfect non-conductors of heat and of cold, and
never a chill reaches their little frames until
hunger presses. Then they must find food and
quickly, or they die. When these snowflakes first
come to us they are tinged with gray and brown,
but gradually through the winter their colours
become more clear-cut and brilliant, until, when
spring comes, they are garbed in contrasting
black and white. With all this change, however,
they leave never a feather with us, but only the
minute brown tips of the feather vanes, which, by
wearing away, leave exposed the clean new
colours beneath.

Thus we find that there are problems innumerable to verify and to solve, even when the tide of
the year's life is at its lowest ebb.

> From out the white and pulsing storm
>   I hear the snowbirds calling;
>   The sheeted winds stalk o'er the hills,
>   And fast the snow is falling.

> •   •   •   •   •   •   •

On twinkling wings they eddy past,
  At home amid the drifting,
Or seek the hills and weedy fields
  Where fast the snow is sifting.

Their coats are dappled white and brown
  Like fields in winter weather,
But on the azure sky they float
  Like snowflakes knit together.

I've heard them on the spotless hills
  Where fox and hound were playing,
The while I stood with eager ear
  Bent on the distant baying.

The unmown fields are their preserves,
  Where weeds and grass are seeding;
They know the lure of distant stacks
  Where houseless herds are feeding.

                              JOHN BURROUGHS.

LET us suppose that a heavy snow has fallen and that we have been a-birding in vain. For once it seems as if all the birds had gone the way of the butterflies. But we are not true bird-lovers unless we can substitute nature for bird whenever the occasion demands; specialisation is only for the ultra-scientist.

There is more to be learned in a snowy field than volumes could tell. There is the tangle of footprints to unravel, the history of the pastimes and foragings and tragedies of the past night writ large and unmistakable. Though the sun now shines brightly, we can well imagine the cold darkness of six hours ago; we can reconstruct the whole scene from those tiny tracks, showing frantic leaps, the indentation of two wing-tips,—a speck of blood. But let us take a bird's-eye view of things, from a bird's-head height; that is, lie flat upon a board or upon the clean, dry crystals and see what wonders we have passed by all our lives.

Take twenty square feet of snow with a stream-let through the centre, and we have an epitome of geological processes and conditions. With chin upon mittens and mittens upon the crust, the eye

opens upon a new world. The half-covered rivu-
let becomes a monster glacier-fed stream, rushing
down through grand canyons and caves, hung with
icy stalactites. Bit by bit the walls are undermined and massive icebergs become detached and
are whirled away. As for moraines, we have them
in plenty; only the windrows of thousands upon
thousands of tiny seeds of which they are composed, are not permanent, but change their form
and position with every strong gust of wind. And
with every gust too their numbers increase, the
harvest of the weeds being garnered here, upon
barren ground. No wonder the stream will be
hidden from view next summer, when the myriad
seeds sprout and begin to fight upward for light
and air.

If we cannot hope for polar bears to complete
our Arctic scene, we may thrill at the sight of a
sinuous weasel, winding his way among the
weeds; and if we look in vain for swans, we at
least may rejoice in a whirling, white flock of snow
buntings.

A few flakes fall gently upon our sleeve and
another world opens before us. A small hand-
lens will be of service, although sharp eyes may
dispense with it. Gather a few recently fallen
flakes upon a piece of black cloth, and the lens will
reveal jewels more beautiful than any ever
fashioned by the hand of man. Six-pointed crystals, always hexagonal, of a myriad patterns,

leave us lost in wonderment when we look out over
the white landscape and think of the hidden beauty
of it all. The largest glacier of Greenland or
Alaska is composed wholly of just such crystals
whose points have melted and which have become
ice.

We may draw or photograph scores of these
beautiful crystals and never duplicate a figure.
Some are almost solid and tabular, others are
simple stars or fern-branched. Then we may
detect compound forms, crystals within crystals,
and, rarest of all, doubles, where two different
forms appear as joined together by a tiny pillar.
In all of these we have an epitome of the crystals
of the rocks beneath our feet, only in their case
the pressure has moulded them into straight col-
umns, while the snow, forming unhindered in mid-
air, resolves itself into these exquisite forms and
floral designs. Flowers and rocks are not so very
unlike after all.

Few of us can observe these wonderful forms
without feeling the poetry of it all. Thoreau on
the fifth day of January, 1856, writes as follows:
. . . "The thin snow now driving from the north
and lodging on my coat consists of those beautiful star crystals, not cottony and chubby spokes
as on the 13th of December, but thin and partly
transparent crystals. They are about one tenth
of an inch in diameter, perfect little wheels with
six spokes, without a tire, or rather with six per-

fect little leaflets, fern-like, with a distinct, straight, slender midrib raying from the centre. On each side of each midrib there is a transparent, thin blade with a crenate edge. How full of the creative genius is the air in which these are generated! I should hardly admire more if real stars fell and lodged on my coat. Nature is full of genius, full of the divinity, so that not a snow-flake escapes its fashioning hand. Nothing is cheap and coarse, neither dewdrops nor snow-flakes. Soon the storm increases (it was already very severe to face), and the snow becomes finer, more white and powdery.

"Who knows but this is the original form of all snowflakes, but that, when I observe these crystal stars falling around me, they are only just generated in the low mist next the earth. I am nearer to the source of the snow, its primal auroral, and golden hour of infancy; commonly the flakes reach us travel-worn and agglomerated, comparatively, without order or beauty, far down in their fall, like men in their advanced age. As for the circumstances under which this occurs, it is quite cold, and the driving storm is bitter to face, though very little snow is falling. It comes almost horizontally from the north. . . . A divinity must have stirred within them, before the crystals did thus shoot and set: wheels of the storm chariots. The same law that shapes the earth and the stars shapes the snowflake. Call it rather snow star.

As surely as the petals of a flower are numbered,
each of these countless snow stars comes whirling
to earth, pronouncing thus with emphasis the
number six, order, κοσμος. This was the beginning of a storm which reached far and wide, and
elsewhere was more severe than here. On the
Saskatchewan, where no man of science is present
to behold, still down they come, and not the less
fulfil their destiny, perchance melt at once on the
Indian's face. What a world we live in, where
myriads of these little discs, so beautiful to the
most prying eye, are whirled down on every
traveller's coat, the observant and the unobserv-
ant, on the restless squirrel's fur, on the far-
stretching fields and forests, the wooded dells and
the mountain tops. Far, far away from the haunts
of men, they roll down some little slope, fall over
and come to their bearings, and melt or lose their
beauty in the mass, ready anon to swell some little
rill with their contribution, and so, at last, the
universal ocean from which they came. There
they lie, like the wreck of chariot wheels after a
battle in the skies. Meanwhile the meadow mouse
shoves them aside in his gallery, the schoolboy
casts them in his ball, or the woodman's sled
glides smoothly over them, these glorious
spangles, the sweepings of heaven's floor. And
they all sing, melting as they sing, of the mysteries
of the number six; six, six, six. He takes up the
waters of the sea in his hand, leaving the salt; he

disperses it in mist through the skies; he re-collects and sprinkles it like grain in six-rayed snowy stars over the earth, there to lie till he dissolves its bonds again.''

But here is a bit of snow which seems less pure, with grayish patches here and there. Down again to sparrow-level and bring the glass to bear. Your farmer friend will tell you that they are snow-fleas which are snowed down with the flakes; the entomologist will call them *Achorutes nivicola* and he knows that they have prosaically wiggled their way from the crevices of bark on the nearest tree-trunk. One's thrill of pleasure at this unexpected discovery will lead one to adopt sparrow-views whenever larger game is lacking.

I walked erstwhile upon thy frozen waves,
And heard the streams amid thy ice-locked caves;
I peered down thy crevasses blue and dim,
Standing in awe upon the dizzy rim.
Beyond me lay the inlet still and blue,
Behind, the mountains loomed upon the view
Like storm-wraiths gathered from the low-hung sky.
A gust of wind swept past with heavy sigh,
And lo! I listened to the ice-stream's song
Of winter when the nights grow dark and long,
And bright stars flash above thy fields of snow,
The cold waste sparkling in the pallid glow.
CHARLES KEELER.

CEDAR BIRDS AND BERRIES

KEEP sharp eyes upon the cedar groves in mid-winter, and sooner or later you will see the waxwings come, not singly or in pairs, but by dozens, and sometimes in great flocks. They will well repay all the watching one gives them. The cedar waxwing is a strange bird, with a very pronounced species-individuality, totally unlike any other bird of our country. When feeding on their favourite winter berries, these birds show to great advantage; the warm rich brown of the upper parts and of the crest contrasting with the black, scarlet, and yellow, and these, in turn, with the dark green of the cedar and the white of the snow.

The name waxwing is due to the scarlet ornaments at the tips of the lesser flight feathers and some of the tail feathers, which resemble bits of red sealing wax, but which are really the bare, flattened ends of the feather shafts. Cherry-bird is another name which is appropriately applied to the cedar waxwing.

These birds are never regular in their movements, and they come and go without heed to weather or date. They should never be lightly passed by, but their flocks carefully examined, lest among their ranks may be hidden a Bohemian chatterer—a stately waxwing larger than common and even more beautiful in hue, whose large size and splashes of white upon its wings will always mark it out.

This bird is one of our rarest of rare visitors, breeding in the far north; and even in its nest and eggs mystery enshrouds it. Up to fifty years ago, absolutely nothing was known of its nesting habits, although during migration Bohemian chatterers are common all over Europe. At last Lapland was found to be their home, and a nest has been found in Alaska and several others in Labrador. My only sight of these birds was of a pair perched in an elm tree in East Orange, New Jersey; but I will never forget it, and will never cease to hope for another such red-letter day.

The movements of the cedar waxwings are as uncertain in summer as they are in winter; they may be common in one locality for a year or two, and then, apparently without reason, desert it. At this season they feed on insects instead of berries, and may be looked for in small flocks in orchard or wood. The period of nesting is usually late, and, in company with the goldfinches, they do not begin their house-keeping until July and August. Unlike other birds, waxwings will build their nests of almost anything near at hand, and apparently in any growth which takes their fancy,—apple, oak, or cedar. The nests are well constructed, however, and often, with their contents, add

another background of a most pleasing harmony
of colours. A nest composed entirely of pale
green hanging moss, with eggs of bluish gray,
spotted and splashed with brown and black,
guarded by a pair of these exquisite birds, is a
sight to delight the eye.

When the young have left the nest, if alarmed
by an intruder, they will frequently, trusting to
their protective dress of streaky brown, freeze
into most unbird-like attitudes, drawing the
feathers close to the body and stretching the neck
stiffly upward,—almost bittern-like. Undoubtedly
other interesting habits which these strangely
picturesque birds may possess are still awaiting
discovery by some enthusiastic observer with a
pair of opera-glasses and a stock of that ever
important characteristic—patience.

Although, during the summer months, myriads
of insects are killed and eaten by the cedar waxwings, yet these birds are pre-eminently berry
eaters,—choke-cherries, cedar berries, blueber-
ries, and raspberries being preferred. Watch a
flock of these birds in a cherry tree, and you will
see the pits fairly rain down. We need not place
our heads, à la Newton, in the path of these falling
stones to deduce some interesting facts,—indeed
to solve the very destiny of the fruit. Many whole
cherries are carried away by the birds to be devoured elsewhere, or we may see parent waxwings

filling their gullets with ten or a dozen berries and carrying them to the eager nestlings.

Thus is made plain the why and the wherefore of the coloured skin, the edible flesh, and the hidden stone of the fruit. The conspicuous racemes of the choke-cherries, or the shining scarlet globes of the cultivated fruit, fairly shout aloud to the birds—"Come and eat us, we're as good as we look!" But Mother Nature looks on and laughs to herself. Thistle seeds are blown to the land's end by the wind; the heavier ticks and burrs are carried far and wide upon the furry coats of passing creatures; but the cherry could not spread its progeny beyond a branch's length, were it not for the ministrations of birds. With birds, as with some other bipeds, the shortest way to the heart is through the stomach, and a choke-cherry tree in full blaze of fruit is always a natural aviary. Where a cedar bird has built its nest, there look some day to see a group of cherry trees; where convenient fence-perches along the roadside lead past cedar groves, there hope before long to see a bird-planted avenue of cedars. And so the marvels of Nature go on evolving,—wheels within wheels.

THE DARK DAYS OF INSECT LIFE

SOMETIMES by too close and confining study of things pertaining to the genus *Homo,* we perchance find ourselves complacently wondering if we have not solved almost all the problems of this little whirling sphere of water and earth. Our minds turn to the ultra questions of atoms and ions and rays and our eyes strain restlessly upward toward our nearest planet neighbour, in half admission that we must soon take up the study of Mars from sheer lack of earthly conquest.

If so minded, hie you to the nearest grove and, digging down through the mid-winter's snow, bring home a spadeful of leaf-mould. Examine it carefully with hand-lens and microscope, and then prophesy what warmth and light will bring forth. Watch the unfolding life of plant and animal, and then come from your planet-yearning back to earth, with a humbleness born of a realisation of our vast ignorance of the commonest things about us.

Though the immediate mysteries of the seed and the egg baffle us, yet the most casual lover of God's out-of-doors may hopefully attempt to solve the question of some of the winter homes of insects. Think of the thousands upon thousands of eggs and pupæ which are hidden in every grove; what catacombs of bug mummies yonder log conceals,—mummies whose resurrection will be brought about by the alchemy of thawing sunbeams. Follow out the suggestion hinted at above and place a handkerchief full of frozen mould or decayed wood in a white dish, and the tiny universe which will gradually unfold before you will provide many hours of interest. But remember your responsibilities in so doing, and do not let the tiny plant germs languish and die for want of water, or the feeble, newly-hatched insects perish from cold or lack a bit of scraped meat.

Cocoons are another never-ending source of delight. If you think that there are no unsolved problems of the commonest insect life around us, say why it is that the moths and millers pass the winter wrapped in swaddling clothes of densest textures, roll upon roll of silken coverlets; while our delicate butterflies hang uncovered, suspended only by a single loop of silk, exposed to the cold blast of every northern gale? Why do the caterpillars of our giant moths—the mythologically named Cecropia, Polyphemus, Luna, and Prometheus—show such individuality in the position which they choose for their temporary shrouds? Protection and concealment are the watchwords held to in each case, but how differently they are achieved!

Cecropia—that beauty whose wings, fully six

inches across, will flap gracefully through the summer twilight—weaves about himself a half oval mound, along some stem or tree-trunk, and becomes a mere excrescence—the veriest un-edible thing a bird may spy. Polyphemus wraps miles of finest silk about his green worm-form (how, even though we watch him do it, we can only guess); weaving in all the surrounding leaves he can reach. This, of course, before the frosts come, but when the leaves at last shrivel, loosen, and their petioles break, it is merely a larger brown nut than usual that falls to the ground, the kernel of which will sprout next June and blossom into the big moth of delicate fawn tints, feathery horned, with those strange isinglass windows in his hind wings.

Luna—the weird, beautiful moon-moth, whose pale green hues and long graceful streamers make us realise how much beauty we miss if we neglect the night life of summer—when clad in her temporary shroud of silk, sometimes falls to the ground, or again the cocoon remains in the tree or bush where it was spun.

But Prometheus, the smallest of the quartet, has a way all his own. The elongated cocoon, looking like a silken finger, is woven about a leaf of sassafras. Even the long stem of the leaf is silk-girdled, and a strong band is looped about the twig to which the leaf is attached. Here, when all the leaves fall, he hangs, the plaything of every breeze, attracting the attention of all the hungry birds. But little does Prometheus care. Sparrows may hover about him and peck in vain; chickadees may clutch the dangling finger and pound with all their tiny might. Prometheus is "bound," indeed, and merely swings the faster, up and down, from side to side.

It is interesting to note that when two Prometheus cocoons, fastened upon their twigs, were suspended in a large cageful of native birds, it took a healthy chickadee just three days of hard pounding and unravelling to force a way through the silken envelopes to the chrysalids within. Such long continued and persistent labour for so comparatively small a morsel of food would not be profitable or even possible out-of-doors in winter. The bird would starve to death while forcing its way through the protecting silk.

These are only four of the many hundreds of cocoons, from the silken shrouds on the topmost branches to the jugnecked chrysalis of a sphinx moth—offering us the riddle of a winter's shelter buried in the cold, dark earth.

Is everything frozen tight? Has Nature's frost mortar cemented every stone in its bed? Then cut off the solid cups of the pitcher plants, and see what insects formed the last meal of these strange growths,—ants, flies, bugs, encased in ice like the fossil insects caught in the amber sap which flowed so many thousands of years ago.

When the fierce northwestern blast
Cools sea and land so far and fast,
Thou already slumberest deep;
Woe and want thou canst outsleep.

EMERSON.

CHAMELEONS IN FUR AND FEATHER

THE colour of things in nature has been the subject of many volumes and yet it may be truthfully said that no two naturalists are wholly agreed on the interpretation of the countless hues of plants and animals. Some assert that all alleged instances of protective colouring and mimicry are merely the result of accident; while at the opposite swing of the pendulum we find theories, protective and mimetic, for the colours of even the tiny one-celled green plants which cover the bark of trees! Here is abundant opportunity for any observer of living nature to help toward the solution of these problems.

In a battle there are always two sides and at its finish one side always runs away while the other pursues. Thus it is in the wars of nature, only here the timid ones are always ready to flee, while the strong are equally prepared to pursue. It is only by constant vigilance that the little mice can save themselves from disappearing down the throats of their enemies, as under cover of darkness they snatch nervous mouthfuls of grain in the fields,—and hence their gray colour and their large, watchful eyes; but on the other hand, the baby owls in their hollow tree would starve if the parents were never able to swoop down in the darkness and surprise a mouse now and then,— hence the gray plumage and great eyes of the parent owls.

The most convincing proof of the reality of protective coloration is in the change of plumage or fur of some of the wild creatures to suit the season. In the far north, the grouse or ptarmigan, as they are called, do not keep feathers of the same colour the year round, as does our ruffed grouse; but change their dress no fewer than three times. When rocks and moss are buried deep beneath the snow, and a keen-eyed hawk appears, the white-feathered ptarmigan crouches and becomes an inanimate mound. Later in the year, with the increasing warmth, patches of gray and brown earth appear, and simultaneously, as if its feathers were really snowflakes, splashes of brown replace the pure white of the bird's plumage, and equally baffle the eye. Seeing one of these birds by itself, we could readily tell, from the colour of its plumage, the time of year and general aspect of the country from which it came. Its plumage is like a mirror which reflects the snow, the moss, or the lichens in turn. It is, indeed, a feathered chameleon, but with changes of colour taking place more slowly than is the case in the reptile.

We may discover changes somewhat similar, but furry instead of feathery, in the woods about our home. The fiercest of all the animals of our continent still evades the exterminating inroads of man; indeed it often puts his traps to shame, and wages destructive warfare in his very midst. I speak of the weasel,—the least of all his family, and yet, for his size, the most bloodthirsty and widely dreaded little demon of all the country-side. His is a name to conjure with among all the lesser wood-folk; the scent of his passing brings an almost helpless paralysis. And yet in some way he must be handicapped, for his slightly larger cousin, the mink, finds good hunting the year round, clad in a suit of rich brown; while the weasel, at the approach of winter, sheds his summer dress of chocolate hue and dons a pure white fur, a change which would seem to put the poor mice and rabbits at a hopeless disadvantage. Nevertheless the ermine, as he is now called (although wrongly so), seems just able to hold his own, with all his evil slinking motions and blood-thirsty desires; for foxes, owls, and hawks take, in their turn, heavy toll. Nature is ever a repetition of the "House that Jack built";—this is the owl that ate the weasel that killed the mouse, and so on.

The little tail-tips of milady's ermine coat are black; and herein lies an interesting fact in the coloration of the weasel and one that, perhaps, gives a clue to some other hitherto inexplicable spots and markings on the fur, feathers, skin, and scales of wild creatures. Whatever the season,

and whatever the colour of the weasel's coat,—
brown or white,—the tip of the tail remains
always black. This would seem, at first thought,
a very bad thing for the little animal. Knowing
so little of fear, he never tucks his tail between
his legs, and, when shooting across an open
expanse of snow, the black tip ever trailing after
him would seem to mark him out for destruction
by every observing hawk or fox.

But the very opposite is the case as Mr. Witmer
Stone so well relates. "If you place a weasel in
its winter white on new-fallen snow, in such a
position that it casts no shadow, you will find that
the black tip of the tail catches your eye and holds
it in spite of yourself, so that at a little distance
it is very difficult to follow the outline of the rest
of the animal. Cover the tip of the tail with snow
and you can see the rest of the weasel itself
much more clearly; but as long as the black
point is in sight, you see that, and that only.

"If a hawk or owl, or any other of the larger
hunters of the woodland, were to give chase to a
weasel and endeavour to pounce upon it, it would
in all probability be the black tip of the tail it
would see and strike at, while the weasel, darting
ahead, would escape. It may, morever, serve as
a guide, enabling the young weasels to follow their
parents more readily through grass and brambles.

"One would suppose that this beautiful white
fur of winter, literally as white as the snow, might

prove a disadvantage at times by making its owner conspicuous when the ground is bare in winter, as it frequently is even in the North; yet though weasels are about more or less by day, you will seldom catch so much as a glimpse of one at such times, though you may hear their sharp chirrup close at hand. Though bold and fearless, they have the power of vanishing instantly, and the slightest alarm sends them to cover. I have seen one standing within reach of my hand in the sunshine on the exposed root of a tree, and while I was staring at it, it vanished like the flame of a candle blown out, without leaving me the slightest clue as to the direction it had taken. All the weasels I have ever seen, either in the woods or open meadows, disappeared in a similar manner.''

To add to the completeness of proof that the change from brown to white is for protection,— in the case of the weasel, both to enable it to escape from the fox and to circumvent the rabbit, —the weasels in Florida, where snow is unknown, do not change colour, but remain brown throughout the whole year.

FEBRUARY

FEBRUARY FEATHERS

FEBRUARY holes are most interesting places and one never knows what will be found in the next one investigated. It is a good plan, in one's walks in the early fall, to make a mental map of all the auspicious looking trees and holes, and then go the rounds of these in winter—as a hunter follows his line of traps. An old, neglected orchard may seem perfectly barren of life; insects dead, leaves fallen, and sap frozen; but the warm hearts of these venerable trees may shelter much beside the larvæ of boring beetles, and we may reap a winter harvest of which the farmer knows nothing.

Poke a stick into a knot-hole and stir up the leaves at the bottom of the cavity, and then look in. Two great yellow eyes may greet you, glaring intermittently, and sharp clicks may assail your ears. Reach in with your gloved hand and bring the screech owl out. He will blink in the sunshine, ruffling up his feathers until he is twice his real size. The light partly blinds him, but toss him into the air and he will fly without difficulty and select with ease a secluded perch. The instant he alights a wonderful transformation comes over him. He stiffens, draws himself as high as possible, and compresses his feathers until he seems naught but the slender, broken stump of some bough,—ragged topped (thanks to his " horns "), gray and lichened. It is little short of a miracle how this spluttering, saucer-eyed, feathered cat can melt away into woody fibre before our very eyes.

We quickly understand why in the daytime the little owl is so anxious to hide his form from public view. Although he can see well enough to fly and to perch, yet the bright sunlight on the snow is too dazzling to permit of swift and sure action. All the birds of the winter woods seem to know this and instantly take advantage of it. Sparrows, chickadees, and woodpeckers go nearly wild with excitement when they discover the little owl, hovering about him and occasionally making darts almost in his very face. We can well believe that as the sun sets, after an afternoon of such excitement, they flee in terror, selecting for that night's perch the densest tangle of sweetbrier to be found.

One hollow tree may yield a little gray owl, while from the next we may draw a red one; and the odd thing about this is that this difference in colour does not depend upon age, sex, or season, and no ornithologist can say why it occurs. What can these little fellows find to feed upon these cold nights, when the birds seek the most hidden and sheltered retreats? We might murder the next owl we come across; but would any fact we might discover in his poor stomach repay us for the thought of having needlessly cut short his life, with its pleasures and spring courtships, and the delight he will take in the half a dozen pearls over which he will soon watch?

A much better way is to examine the ground around his favourite roosting place, where we will find many pellets of fur and bones, with now and then a tiny skull. These tell the tale, and if at dusk we watch closely, we may see the screech owl look out of his door, stretch every limb, purr his shivering song, and silently launch out over the fields, a feathery, shadowy death to all small mice who scamper too far from their snow tunnels.

When you feel like making a new and charming acquaintance, take your way to a dense clump of snow-laden cedars, and look carefully over their trunks. If you are lucky you will spy a tiny gray form huddled close to the sheltered side of the bark, and if you are careful you may approach and catch in your hand the smallest of all our owls, for the saw-whet is a dreadfully sleepy fellow in the daytime. I knew of eleven of these little gray gnomes dozing in a clump of five small cedars.

The cedars are treasure-houses in winter, and many birds find shelter among the thick foliage, and feast upon the plentiful supply of berries, when elsewhere there seems little that could keep a bird's life in its body. When the tinkling of breaking icicles is taken up by the wind and re-echoed from the tops of the cedars, you may know that a flock of purple finches is near, and so greedy and busy are they that you may approach within a few feet. These birds are unfortunately named, as there is nothing purple about their plumage. The males are a delicate rose-red, while the females look like commonplace sparrows, streaked all over with black and brown.

There are other winter birds, whose home is in the North, with a similar type of coloration. Among the pines you may see a flock of birds, as large as a sparrow, with strange-looking beaks. The tips of the two mandibles are long, curved, and pointed, crossing each other at their ends. This looks like a deformity, but is in reality a splendid cone-opener and seed-extracter. These birds are the crossbills.

Even in the cold of a February day, we may, on very rare occasions, be fortunate enough to hear unexpected sounds, such as the rattle of a belted kingfisher, or the croak of a night heron; for these birds linger until every bit of pond or lake is sealed with ice; and when a thaw comes, a lonely bat may surprise us with a short flight through the frosty air, before it returns to its winter's trance.

Of course, in the vicinity of our towns and cities, the most noticeable birds at this season of the year (as indeed at all seasons) are the English sparrows and (at least near New York City) the starlings, those two foreigners which have wrought such havoc among our native birds. Their mingled flocks fly up, not only from garbage piles and gutters, but from the thickets and fields which should be filled with our sweet-voiced American birds. It is no small matter for man heedlessly to interfere with Nature. What may be a harmless, or even useful, bird in its native land may prove a terrible scourge when introduced where there are no enemies to keep it in check. Nature is doing her best to even matters by letting albinism run riot among the sparrows, and best of all by teaching sparrow hawks to nest under our eaves and thus be on equal terms with their sparrow prey. The starlings are turning out to be worse than the sparrows. Already they are invading the haunts of our grackles and red-wings.

On some cold day, when the sun is shining, visit all the orchards of which you know, and see if in one or more you cannot find a good-sized, gray, black, and white bird, which keeps to the topmost branch of a certain tree. Look at him carefully through your glasses, and if his beak is hooked, like that of a hawk, you may know that you are watching a northern shrike, or butcher bird. His manner is that of a hawk, and his appearance causes instant panic among small birds. If you watch long enough you may see him pursue and kill a goldfinch, or sparrow, and devour it. These

birds are not even distantly related to the hawks,
but have added a hawk's characteristics and appe-
tite to the insect diet of their nearest relations.
If ever shrikes will learn to confine their attacks
to English sparrows, we should offer them every
encouragement.

All winter long the ebony forms of crows vibrate
back and forth across the cold sky. If we watch
them when very high up, we sometimes see them
sail a short distance, and without fail, a second
later, the clear *"Caw! caw!"* comes down to us,
the sound-waves unable to keep pace with those
of light, as the thunder of the storm lags behind
the flash. These sturdy birds seem able to stand
any severity of the weather, but, like Achilles, they
have one vulnerable point, the eyes,—which, during the long winter nights, must be kept deep
buried among the warm feathers.

FISH LIFE

WE have all looked down through the clear water of brook or pond and watched the gracefully poised trout or pickerel; but have we ever tried to imagine what the life of one of these aquatic beings is really like? "Water Babies" perhaps gives us the best idea of existence below the water, but if we spend one day each month for a year in trying to imagine ourselves in the place of the fish, we will see that a fish-eye view of life holds much of interest.

What a delightful sensation must it be to all but escape the eternal downpull of gravity, to float and turn and rise and fall at will, and all by the least twitch of tail or limb,—for fish have limbs, four of them, as truly as has a dog or horse, only instead of fingers or toes there are many delicate rays extending through the fin. These four limb-fins are useful chiefly as balancers, while the tail-fin is what sends the fish darting through the water, or turns it to right or left, with incredible swiftness.

If we were able to examine some inhabitant of the planet Mars our first interest would be to know with what senses they were endowed, and these finny creatures living in their denser medi-

um, which after a few seconds would mean death
to us, excite the same interest. They see, of
course, having eyes, but do they feel, hear, and
smell?

Probably the sense of taste is least developed.
When a trout leaps at and catches a fly he does
not stop to taste, otherwise the pheasant feather
concealing the cruel hook would be of little use.
When an animal catches its food in the water and
swallows it whole, taste plays but a small part.
Thus the tongue of a pelican is a tiny flap all but
lost to view in its great bill.

Water is an excellent medium for carrying minute particles of matter and so the sense of smell
is well developed. A bit of meat dropped into the
sea will draw the fish from far and wide, and a
slice of liver will sometimes bring a score
of sharks and throw them into the greatest
excitement.

Fishes are probably very near-sighted, but that
they can distinguish details is apparent in the
choice which a trout exhibits in taking certain
coloured artificial flies. We may suppose from
what we know of physics that when we lean over
and look down into a pool, the fishy eyes which
peer up at us discern only a dark, irregular mass.
I have seen a pickerel dodge as quickly at a sudden
cloud-shadow as at the motion of a man wielding
a fish pole.

We can be less certain about the hearing of

fishes. They have, however, very respectable inner ears, built on much the same plan as in higher animals. Indeed many fish, such as the grunts, make various sounds which are plainly audible even to our ears high above the water, and we cannot suppose that this is a useless accomplishment. But the ears of fishes and the line of tiny tubes which extends along the side may be more effective in recording the tremors of the water transmitted by moving objects than actual sound.

Watch a lazy catfish winding its way along near the bottom, with its barbels extended, and you will at once realise that fishes can feel, this function being very useful to those kinds which search for their food in the mud at the bottom.

.   .   .   .

Not a breath of air stirs the surface of the woodland pond, and the trees about the margin are reflected unbroken in its surface. The lilies and their pads lie motionless, and in and out through the shadowy depths, around the long stems, float a school of half a dozen little sunfish. They move slowly, turning from side to side all at once as if impelled by one idea. Now and then one will dart aside and snap up a beetle or mosquito larva, then swing back to its place among its fellows. Their beautiful scales flash scarlet, blue, and gold, and their little hand-and-foot fins are ever trembling and waving. They drift upward nearer the

surface, the wide round eyes turning and twisting in their sockets, ever watchful for food and
danger. Without warning a terrific splash scatters them, and when the ripples and bubbles cease,
five frightened sunfish cringe in terror among the
water plants of the bottom mud. Off to her nest
goes the kingfisher, bearing to her brood the
struggling sixth.

Later in the day, when danger seemed far off,
a double-pointed vise shot toward the little group
of "pumpkin seeds" and a great blue heron swallowed one of their number. Another, venturing
too far beyond the protection of the lily stems and
grass tangle of the shallows, fell victim to a vora-
cious pickerel. But the most terrible fate befell
when one day a black sinuous body came swiftly
through the water. The fish had never seen its
like before and yet some instinct told them that
here was death indeed and they fled as fast as
their fins could send them. The young otter had
marked the trio and after it he sped, turning,
twisting, following every movement with never a
stop for breath until he had caught his prey.

But the life of a fish is not all tragedy, and the
two remaining sunfish may live in peace. In
spawning time they clear a little space close to
the water of the inlet, pulling up the young weeds
and pushing up the sandy bottom until a hollow,
bowl-like nest is prepared. Thoreau tells us that
here the fish "may be seen early in summer

assiduously brooding, and driving away minnows and larger fishes, even its own species, which would disturb its ova, pursuing them a few feet, and circling round swiftly to its nest again; the minnows, like young sharks, instantly entering the empty nests, meanwhile, and swallowing the spawn, which is attached to the weeds and to the bottom, on the sunny side. The spawn is exposed to so many dangers that a very small proportion can ever become fishes, for beside being the constant prey of birds and fishes, a great many nests are made so near the shore, in shallow water, that they are left dry in a few days, as the river goes down. These and the lampreys are the only fishes' nests that I have observed, though the ova of some species may be seen floating on the surface. The sunfish are so careful of their charge that you may stand close by in the water and examine them at your leisure. I have thus stood over them half an hour at a time, and stroked them familiarly without frightening them, suffering them to nibble my fingers harmlessly, and seen them erect their dorsal fins in anger when my hand approached their ova, and have even taken them gently out of the water with my hand; though this cannot be accomplished by a sudden movement, however dexterous, for instant warning is conveyed to them through their denser element, but only by letting the fingers gradually close about them as they are poised over the palm, and with the

utmost gentleness raising them slowly to the surface. Though stationary, they kept up a constant
sculling or waving motion with their fins, which is
exceedingly graceful, and expressive of their
humble happiness; for unlike ours, the element in
which they live is a stream which must be constantly resisted. From time to time they nibble
the weeds at the bottom or overhanging their
nests, or dart after a fly or worm. The dorsal
fin, besides answering the purpose of a keel, with
the anal, serves to keep the fish upright, for in
shallow water, where this is not covered, they fall
on their sides. As you stand thus stooping over
the sunfish in its nest, the edges of the dorsal and
caudal fins have a singular dusty golden reflec-
tion, and its eyes, which stand out from the head,
are transparent and colourless. Seen in its native
element, it is a very beautiful and compact fish,
perfect in all its parts, and looks like a brilliant
coin fresh from the mint. It is a perfect jewel of
the river, the green, red, coppery, and golden
reflections of its mottled sides being the concen-
tration of such rays as struggle through the floating pads and flowers to the sandy bottom, and in
harmony with the sunlit brown and yellow
pebbles.''

When the cold days of winter come and the ice
begins to close over the pond, the sunfish become
sluggish and keep near the bottom, half-hibernat-
ing but not unwilling to snap at any bit of food

which may drift near them. Lying prone on the
ice we may see them poising with slowly undulating fins, waiting, in their strange wide-eyed sleep,
for the warmth which will bring food and active
life again.

3rd. *Fish*. Master, I marvel how the fishes live in the sea.
1st. *Fish*. Why, as men do a-land: the great ones eat up
the little ones.

SHAKESPEARE.

TENANTS OF WINTER BIRDS' NESTS

WHEN we realise how our lives are hedged about by butchers, bakers, and luxury-makers, we often envy the wild creatures their independence. And yet, although each animal is capable of finding its own food and shelter and of avoiding all ordinary danger, there is much dependence, one upon another, among the little creatures of fur and feathers.

The first instinct of a gray squirrel, at the approach of winter, is to seek out a deep, warm, hollow limb, or trunk. Nowadays, however, these are not to be found in every grove. The precepts of modern forestry decree that all such unsightly places must be filled with cement and creosote and well sealed against the entrance of rain and snow. When hollows are not available, these hardy squirrels prepare their winter home in another way. Before the leaves have begun to loosen on their stalks, the little creatures set to work. The crows have long since deserted their rough nest of sticks in the top of some tall tree, and now the squirrels come, investigate, and adopt the forsaken bird's-nest as the foundation of their home. The sticks are pressed more tightly together, all interstices filled up, and then a superstructure of leafy twigs is woven overhead and all around. The leaves on

these twigs, killed before their time, do not fall;
and when the branches of the tree become bare,
there remains in one of the uppermost crotches a
big ball of leaves,—rain and snow proof, with a
tiny entrance at one side.

On a stormy mid-winter afternoon we stand
beneath the tree and, through the snowflakes
driven past by the howling gale, we catch glimpses
of the nest swaying high in air. Far over it
leans, as the branches are whipped and bent by
the wind, and yet so cunningly is it wrought that
never a twig or leaf loosens. We can imagine the
pair of little shadow-tails within, sleeping fearlessly throughout all the coming night.

But the sleep of the gray squirrel is a healthy
and a natural one, not the half-dead trance of
hibernation; and early next morning their sharp
eyes appear at the entrance of their home and
they are out and off through the tree-top path
which only their feet can traverse. Down the
snowy trunks they come with a rush, and with
strong, clean bounds they head unerringly for
their little *caches* of nuts. Their provender is
hidden away among the dried leaves, and when
they want a nibble of nut or acorn they make their
way, by some mysterious sense, even through
three feet of snow, down to the bit of food which,
months before, they patted out of sight among the
moss and leaves.

It would seem that some exact sub-conscious

sense of locality would be a more probable solution of this feat than the sense of smell, however keenly developed, when we consider that dozens of nuts may be hidden or buried in close proximity to the one sought by the squirrel.

Even though the birds seem to have vanished from the earth, and every mammal be deeply buried in its long sleep, no winter's walk need be barren of interest. A suggestion worth trying would be to choose a certain area of saplings and underbrush and proceed systematically to fathom every cause which has prevented the few stray leaves still upon their stalks from falling with their many brethren now buried beneath the snow.

The encircling silken bonds of Promethea and Cynthia cocoons will account for some; others will puzzle us until we have found the traces of some insect foe, whose girdling has killed the twig and thus prevented the leaf from falling at the usual time; some may be simply mechanical causes, where a broken twig crotch has fallen athwart another stem in the course of its downward fall. Then there is the pitiful remnant of a last summer's bird's-nest, with a mere skeleton of a floor all but disintegrated.

But occasionally a substantial ball of dead leaves will be noticed, swung amid a tangle of brier. No accident lodged these, nor did any insect have aught to do with their position. Examine carefully the mass of leaves and you will find a replica of the gray squirrel's nest, only, of course, much smaller. This handiwork of the white-footed or deer mouse can be found in almost every field or tangle of undergrowth; the nest of a field sparrow or catbird being used as a foundation and thickly covered over and tightly thatched with leaves. Now and then, even in mid-winter, we may find the owner at home, and as the weasel is the most bloodthirsty, so the deer mouse is the most beautiful and gentle of all the fur-coated folk of our woods. With his coat of white and pale golden brown and his great black, lustrous eyes, and his timid, trusting ways, he is altogether lovable.

He spends the late summer and early autumn in his tangle-hung home, but in winter he generally selects a snug hollow log, or some cavity in the earth. Here he makes a round nest of fine grass and upon a couch of thistledown he sleeps in peace, now and then waking to partake of the little hoard of nuts which he has gathered, or he may even dare to frolic about upon the snow in the cold winter moonlight, leaving behind him no trace, save the fairy tracery of his tiny footprints.

> Wee, sleekit, cow'rin', tim'rous beastie,
> O, what a panic's in thy breastie!
> Thou need na start awa sae hasty,
>   Wi' bickering brattle!
> I wad be laith to rin an' chase thee,
> Wi' murd'ring prattle!
>
> Robert Burns.

WINTER HOLES

THE decayed hollows which we have mentioned as so often productive of little owls have their possibilities by no means exhausted by one visit. The disturbed owl may take himself elsewhere, after being so unceremoniously disturbed; but there are roving, tramp-like characters, with dispositions taking them here and there through the winter nights, to whom, at break of day, a hole is ever a sought-for haven.

So do not put your hand too recklessly into an owl hole, for a hiss and a sudden nip may show that an opossum has taken up his quarters there. If you must, pull him out by his squirming, naked tail, but do not carry him home, as he makes a poor pet, and between hen-house traps and irate farmers, he has good reason, in this part of the country at least, to be short tempered.

Of course the birds'-nests are all deserted now, but do not be too sure of the woodpeckers' holes. The little downy and his larger cousin, the hairy woodpecker, often spend the winter nights snug within deep cavities which they have hollowed out, each bird for itself. I have never known a pair to share one of these shelters.

Sometimes, in pulling off the loose bark from a decayed stump, several dry, flattened scales will fall out upon the snow among the débris of wood and dead leaves. Hold them close in the warm palm of your hand for a time and the dried bits will quiver, the sides partly separate, and behold! you have brought back to life a beautiful *Euvanessa,* or mourning-cloak butterfly. Lay it upon the snow and soon the awakened life will ebb away and it will again be stiff, as in death. If you wish, take it home, and you may warm it into activity, feed it upon a drop of syrup and freeze it again at will. Sometimes six or eight of these insects may be found sheltered under the bark of a single stump, or in a hollow beneath a stone. Several species share this habit of hibernating throughout the winter.

Look carefully in old, deserted sheds, in half-sheltered hollows of trees, or in deep crevice-caverns in rocks, and you may some day spy one of the strangest of our woodfolk. A poor little shrivelled bundle of fur, tight-clasped in its own skinny fingers, with no more appearance of life in its frozen body than if it were a mummy from an Egyptian tomb; such is the figure that will meet your eye when you chance upon a bat in the deep trance of its winter's hibernation. Often you will find six or a dozen of these stiffened forms clinging close together, head downward.

As in the case of the sleeping butterfly, carry one of the bats to your warm room and place him in a bird-cage, hanging him up on the top wires by his toes, with his head downward. The inverted position of these strange little beings always brings to mind some of the experiences of Gulliver, and indeed the life of a bat is more wonderful than any fairy tale.

Probably the knowledge of bats which most of us possess is chiefly derived from the imaginations of artists and poets, who, unlike the Chinese, do not look upon these creatures with much favour, generally symbolising them in connection with passages and pictures which relate to the infernal regions. All of which is entirely unjust. Their nocturnal habits and our consequent ignorance of their characteristics are the only causes which can account for their being associated with the realm of Satan. In some places bats are called flittermice, but they are more nearly related to moles, shrews, and other insect-eaters than they are to mice. If we look at the skeleton of an animal which walks or hops we will notice that its hind limbs are much the stronger, and that the girdle which connects these with the backbone is composed of strong and heavy bones. In bats a reverse condition is found; the breast girdle, or bones corresponding to our collar bones and shoulder blades, are greatly developed. This, as in birds, is, of course, an adaptation to give surface for the attachment of the great propelling muscles of the wings.

Although the hand of a bat is so strangely

altered, yet, as we shall see if we look at our captive specimen, it has five fingers, as we have, four of which are very long and thin, and the webs, of which we have a very noticeable trace in our own hands, stretch from finger-tip to finger-tip, and to the body and even down each leg, ending squarely near the ankle, thus giving the creature the absurd appearance of having on a very broad, baggy pair of trousers.

When thoroughly warmed up, our bat will soon start on a tour of inspection of his cage. He steps rapidly from one wire to another, sometimes hooking on with all five toes, but generally with four or three. There seems to be little power in these toes, except of remaining bent in a hooked position; for when our bat stops and draws up one foot to scratch the head, the claws are merely jerked through the fur by motions of the whole leg, not by individual movements of the separate toes. In this motion we notice, for the first time, that the legs and feet grow in a kind of "spread eagle" position, making the knees point backward, in the same direction as the elbows.

We must stop a moment to admire the beautiful soft fur, a golden brown in colour, with part of the back nearly black. The tiny inverted face is full of expression, the bead-like eyes gleaming brightly from out of their furry bed. The small moist nostrils are constantly wrinkling and sniffling, and the large size of the alert ears shows how much their owner depends upon them for information. If we suddenly move up closer to the wires, the bat opens both wings owl-like, in a most threatening manner; but if we make still more hostile motions the creature retreats as hastily as it can, changing its method of progress to an all-fours, sloth-like gait, the long free thumb of each hand grasping wire after wire and doing most of the leverage, the hind legs following passively.

When at what he judges a safe distance he again hangs pendent, bending his head back to look earnestly at us. Soon the half-opened wings are closed and brought close to the shoulders, and in this, the usual resting position, the large claws of the thumbs rest on the breast in little furrows which they have worn in the fur.

Soon drowsiness comes on and a long elaborate yawn is given, showing the many small needle-like teeth and the broad red tongue, which curls outward to a surprising length. Then comes the most curious process of all. Drawing up one leg, the little creature deliberately wraps one hand with its clinging web around the leg and under the arms, and then draws the other wing straight across the body, holds it there a moment, while it takes a last look in all directions. Then lifting its fingers slightly, it bends its head and wraps all in the full-spread web. It is most ludicrously like a tragedian, acting the death scene in ''Julius

Cæsar," and it loses nothing in repetition; for each time the little animal thus draws its winding sheet about its body, one is forced to smile as he thinks of the absurd resemblance.

But all this and much more you will see for yourself, if you are so fortunate as to discover the hiding-place of the hibernating bat.

Our little brown bat is a most excellent mother, and when in summer she starts out on her nocturnal hunts she takes her tiny baby bat with her. The weird little creature wraps his long fingers about his mother's neck and off they go. When two young are born, the father bat is said sometimes to assume entire control of one.

After we come to know more of the admirable family traits of the *fledermaus*—its musical German name—we shall willingly defend it from the calumny which for thousands of years has been heaped upon it.

Hibernation is a strange phenomenon, and one which is but little understood. If we break into the death-like trance for too long a time, or if we do not supply the right kind of food, our captive butterflies and bats will perish. So let us soon freeze them up again and place them back in the care of old Nature. Thus the pleasure is ours of having made them yield up their secrets, without any harm to them. Let us fancy that in the spring they may remember us only as a strange dream which has come to them during their long sleep.

MARCH

FEATHERED PIONEERS

IN the annual war of the seasons, March is the
time of the most bitterly contested battles.
But we—and very likely the birds—can look ahead
and realise what the final outcome will invariably
be, and, our sympathies being on the winning side,
every advance of spring's outposts gladdens our
hearts. But winter is a stubborn foe, and sometimes his snow and icicle battalions will not give
way a foot. Though by day the sun's fierce
attack may drench the earth with the watery
blood of the ice legions, yet at night, silently
and grimly, new reserves of cold repair the
damage.

Our winter visitors are still in force. Amid the
stinging cold the wee brown form of a winter wren
will dodge round a brush pile—a tiny bundle of
energy which defies all chill winds and which
resolves bug chrysalides and frozen insects into
a marvellous activity. Other little birds, as small
as the wren, call to us from the pines and cedars—
golden-crowned kinglets, olive-green of body,
while on their heads burns a crest of orange and
gold.

When a good-sized brown bird flies up before
you, showing a flash of white on his rump, you

may know him for the flicker, the most unwood-pecker-like of his family. He is more or less deserting the tree-climbing method for ground feeding, and if you watch him you will see many habits which his new mode of life is teaching him.

Even in the most wintry of Marches some warm, thawing days are sure to be thrown in between storms, and nothing, not even pussy willows and the skunk cabbage, yield more quickly to the mellowing influence than do the birds—sympathetic brethren of ours that they are. Hardly has the sunniest icicle begun to drop tears, when a song sparrow flits to the top of a bush, clears his throat with sharp chirps and shouts as loud as he can: "Hip! Hip! Hip! Hurrah—!" Even more boreal visitors feel the new influence, and tree and fox sparrows warble sweetly. But the bluebird's note will always be spring's dearest herald. When this soft, mellow sound floats from the nearest fence post, it seems to thaw something out of our ears; from this instant winter seems on the defensive; the crisis has come and gone in an instant, in a single vibration of the air.

Bright colours are still scarce among our birds, but another blue form may occasionally pass us, for blue jays are more noticeable now than at any other time of the year. Although not by any means a rare bird, with us jays are shy and wary. In Florida their southern cousins are as familiar as robins, without a trace of fear of mankind.

What curious notes our blue jays have—a creaking, wheedling, rasping medley of sounds coming through the leafless branches. At this time of year they love acorns and nuts, but in the spring "their fancy turns to thoughts of" eggs and young nestlings, and they are accordingly hated by the small birds. Nevertheless no bird is quicker to shout and scream "Thief! Robber!" at some harmless little owl than are these blue and white rascals.

You may seek in vain to discover the first sign of nesting among the birds. Scarcely has winter set in in earnest, you will think, when the tiger-eyed one of the woods—the great horned owl—will have drifted up to some old hawk's nest, and laid her white spheres fairly in the snow. When you discover her "horns" above the nest lining of dried leaves, you may find that her fuzzy young owls are already hatched. But these owls are an exception, and no other bird in our lattitude cares to risk the dangers of late February or early March.

March is sometimes a woodpecker month, and almost any day one is very likely to see, besides the flicker, the hairy or downy woodpecker. The latter two are almost counterparts of each other, although the downy is the more common. They hammer cheerfully upon the sounding boards which Nature has provided for them, striking slow or fast, soft or loud, as their humour dictates.

Near New York, a day in March—I have found it varying from March 8 to March 12—is "crow day." Now the winter roosts apparently break up, and all day flocks of crows, sometimes thousands upon thousands of them, pass to the northward. If the day is quiet and spring-like, they fly very high, black motes silhouetted against the blue,—but if the day is a "March day," with whistling, howling winds, then the black fellows fly close to earth, rising just enough to clear bushes and trees, and taking leeward advantage of every protection. For days after, many crows pass, but never so many as on the first day, when crow law, or crow instinct, passes the word, we know not how, which is obeyed by all.

For miles around not a drop of water may be found; it seems as if every pool and lake were solid to the bottom, and yet, when we see a large bird, with goose-like body, long neck and long, pointed beak, flying like a bullet of steel through the sky, we may be sure that there is open water to the northward, for a loon never makes a mistake. When the first pioneer of these hardy birds passes, he knows that somewhere beyond us fish can be caught. If we wonder where he has spent the long winter months, we should take a steamer to Florida. Out on the ocean, sometimes a hundred miles or more from land, many of these birds make their winter home. When the bow of the steamer bears down upon one, the bird half spreads its wings, then closes them quickly, and sinks out of sight in the green depths, not to reappear until the steamer has passed, when he looks after us and utters his mocking laugh. Here he will float until the time comes for him to go north. We love the brave fellow, remembering him in his home among the lakes of Canada; but we tremble for him when we think of the terrible storm waves which he must outride, and the sneering sharks which must sometimes spy him. What a story he could tell of his life among the phalaropes and jelly-fishes!

Meadow larks are in flocks in March, and as their yellow breasts, with the central crescent of black, rise from the snow-bent grass, their long, clear, vocal "arrow" comes to us, piercing the air like a veritable icicle of sound. When on the ground they are walkers like the crow.

As the kingfisher and loon appear to know long ahead when the first bit of clear water will appear, so the first insect on the wing seems to be anticipated by a feathered flycatcher. Early some morning, when the wondrous Northern Lights are still playing across the heavens, a small voice may make all the surroundings seem incongruous. Frosty air, rimmed tree-trunks, naked branches, aurora—all seem as unreal as stage properties, when *phœ-be!* comes to our ears. Yes, there is the little dark-feathered, tail-wagging fellow, hungry no doubt, but sure that when the sun warms up, Mother Nature will strew his aerial breakfast-table with tiny gnats,—precocious, but none the less toothsome for all that.

> Hark 'tis the bluebird's venturous strain
>   High on the old fringed elm at the gate—
> Sweet-voiced, valiant on the swaying bough,
>   Alert, elate,
> Dodging the fitful spits of snow,
>   New England's poet-laureate
> Telling us Spring has come again!
>
> THOMAS BAILEY ALDRICH.

THE WAYS OF MEADOW MICE

DAY after day we may walk through the woods and fields, using our eyes as best we can, searching out every moving thing, following up every sound,—and yet we touch only the coarsest, perceive only the grossest of the life about us. Tramp the same way after a fall of snow and we are astonished at the evidences of life of which we knew nothing. Everywhere, in and out among the reed stems, around the tree-trunks, and in wavy lines and spirals all about, runs the delicate tracery of the meadow mice trails. No leapers these, as are the white-footed and jumping mice, but short-legged and stout of body. Yet with all their lack of size and swiftness, they are untiring little folk, and probably make long journeys from their individual nests.

As far north as Canada and west to the Plains the meadow or field mice are found, and everywhere they seem to be happy and content. Most of all, however, they enjoy the vicinity of water, and a damp, half-marshy meadow is a paradise for them. No wonder their worst enemies are known as marsh hawks and marsh owls; these hunters of the daylight and the night well know where the meadow mice love to play.

These mice are resourceful little beings and

when danger threatens they will take to the water without hesitation; and when the muskrat has gone the way of the beaver, our ditches and ponds will not be completely deserted, for the little meadow mice will swim and dive for many years thereafter.

Not only in the meadows about our inland streams, but within sound of the breakers on the seashore, these vigorous bits of fur find bountiful living, and it is said that the mice folk inhabiting these low salt marshes always know in some mysterious way when a disastrous high tide is due, and flee in time, so that when the remorseless ripples lap higher and higher over the wide stretches of salt grass, not a mouse will be drowned. By some delicate means of perception all have been notified in time, and these, among the least of Nature's children, have run and scurried along their grassy paths to find safety on the higher ground.

These paths seem an invention of the meadow mice, and, affording them a unique escape from danger, they doubtless, in a great measure, account for the extreme abundance of the little creatures. When a deer mouse or a chipmunk emerges from its hollow log or underground tunnel, it must take its chances in open air. It may dart along close to the ground or amid an impenetrable tangle of briers, but still it is always visible from above. On the other hand, a mole,

pushing blindly along beneath the sod, fears no
danger from the hawk soaring high overhead.

The method of the meadow mice is between
these two: its stratum of active life is above the
mole and beneath the chipmunk. Scores of sharp
little incisor teeth are forever busy gnawing and
cutting away the tender grass and sprouting
weeds in long meandering paths or trails through
the meadows. As these paths are only a mouse-
breadth in width, the grasses at each side lean
inward, forming a perfect shelter of interlocking
stems overhead. Two purposes are thus fulfilled:
a delicious succulent food is obtained and a way
of escape is kept ever open. These lines intersect
and cross at every conceivable angle, and as the
meadow mice clan are ever friendly toward one
another, any particular mouse seems at liberty
to traverse these miles of mouse alleys.

In winter, when the snow lies deep upon the
ground, these same mice drive tunnels beneath it,
leading to all their favourite feeding grounds, to
all the heavy-seeded weed heads, with which the
bounty of Nature supplies them. But at night
these tunnels are deserted and boldly out upon the
snow come the meadow mice, chasing each other
over its gleaming surface, nibbling the toothsome
seeds, dodging, or trying to dodge, the owl-
shadows; living the keen, strenuous, short, but
happy, life which is that of all the wild meadow
folk.

That wee bit heap o' leaves an' stibble
Has cost thee mony a weary nibble!
Thou saw the fields laid bare and waste,
An' weary winter comin' fast,
An' cosey here, beneath the blast,
    Thou thought to dwell.

                                   ROBERT BURNS.

PROBLEMS OF BIRD LIFE

THE principal problems which birds, and indeed all other creatures, have to solve, have been well stated to be—Food, Safety, and Reproduction. In regard to safety, or the art of escaping danger, we are all familiar with the ravages which hawks, owls, foxes, and even red squirrels commit among the lesser feathered creatures, but there are other dangers which few of us suspect.

Of all creatures birds are perhaps the most exempt from liability to accident, yet they not infrequently lose their lives in most unexpected ways. Once above trees and buildings, they have the whole upper air free of every obstacle, and though their flight sometimes equals the speed of a railroad train, they have little to fear when well above the ground. Collision with other birds seems scarcely possible, although it sometimes does occur. When a covey of quail is flushed, occasionally two birds will collide, at times meeting with such force that both are stunned. Flycatchers darting at the same insect will now and then come together, but not hard enough to injure either bird.

Even the smallest and most wonderful of all

flyers, the hummingbird, may come to grief in accidental ways. I have seen one entangled in a burdock burr, its tiny feathers fast locked into the countless hooks, and again I have found the body of one of these little birds with its bill fastened in a spiral tendril of a grapevine, trapped in some unknown way.

Young phœbes sometimes become entangled in the horsehairs which are used in the lining of their nest. When they are old enough to fly and attempt to leave, they are held prisoners or left dangling from the nest. When mink traps are set in the snow in winter, owls frequently fall victims, mice being scarce and the bait tempting.

Lighthouses are perhaps the cause of more accidents to birds than are any of the other obstacles which they encounter on their nocturnal migrations north and south. Many hundreds of birds are sometimes found dead at the base of these structures. The sudden bright glare is so confusing and blinding, as they shoot from the intense darkness into its circle of radiance, that they are completely bewildered and dash headlong against the thick panes of glass. Telegraph wires are another menace to low-flying birds, especially those which, like quail and woodcock, enjoy a whirlwind flight, and attain great speed within a few yards. Such birds have been found almost cut in two by the force with which they struck the wire.

The elements frequently catch birds unaware and overpower them. A sudden wind or storm will drive coast-flying birds hundreds of miles out to sea, and oceanic birds may be blown as far inland. Hurricanes in the West Indies are said to cause the death of innumerable birds, as well as of other creatures. From such a cause small islands are known to have become completely depopulated of their feathered inhabitants. Violent hailstorms, coming in warm weather without warning, are quite common agents in the destruction of birds, and in a city thousands of English sparrows have been stricken during such a storm. After a violent storm of wet snow in the middle West, myriads of Lapland longspurs were once found dead in the streets and suburbs of several villages. On the surface of two small lakes, a conservative estimate of the dead birds was a million and a half!

The routes which birds follow in migrating north and south sometimes extend over considerable stretches of water, as across the Caribbean Sea, but the only birds which voluntarily brave the dangers of the open ocean are those which, from ability to swim, or great power of flight, can trust themselves far away from land. Not infrequently a storm will drive birds away from the land and carry them over immense distances, and this accounts for the occasional appearance of land birds near vessels far out at sea. Overcome with fatigue, they perch for hours in the rigging before taking flight in the direction of the nearest land, or, desperate from hunger, they fly fearlessly down to the deck, where food and water are seldom refused them.

Small events like these are welcome breaks in the monotony of a long ocean voyage, but are soon forgotten at the end of the trip.

Two of these ocean waifs were once brought to me. One was a young European heron which flew on board a vessel when it was about two hundred and five miles southeast of the southern extremity of India. A storm must have driven the bird seaward, as there is no migration route near this locality.

The second bird was a European turtle dove which was captured not less than seven hundred and fifty miles from the nearest land—Ireland. When caught it was in an exhausted condition, but it quickly recovered and soon lost all signs of the buffeting of the storm. The turtle dove migrates northward to the British Islands about the first of May, but as this bird was captured on May 17th, it was not migrating, but, caught by a gust of wind, was probably blown away from the land. The force of the storm would then drive it mile after mile, allowing it no chance of controlling the direction of its flight, but, from the very velocity, making it easy for the bird to maintain its equilibrium.

Hundreds of birds must perish when left by storms far out at sea, and the infinitely small chance of encountering a vessel or other resting-place makes a bird which has passed through such an experience and survived, interesting indeed.

In winter ruffed grouse have a habit of burrowing deep beneath the snow and letting the storm shut them in. In this warm, cosey retreat they spend the night, their breath making its way out through the loosely packed crystals. But when a cold rain sets in during the night, this becomes a fatal trap, an impenetrable crust cutting off their means of escape.

Ducks, when collected about a small open place in an ice-covered pond, diving for the tender roots on which they feed, sometimes become confused and drown before they find their way out. They have been seen frozen into the ice by hundreds, sitting there helplessly, and fortunate if the sun, with its thawing power, releases them before they are discovered by marauding hawks or foxes.

In connection with their food supply the greatest enemy of birds is ice, and when a winter rain ends with a cold snap, and every twig and seed is encased in a transparent armour of ice, then starvation stalks close to all the feathered kindred. Then is the time to scatter crumbs and grain broadcast, to nail bones and suet to the tree-trunks and so awaken hope and life in the shivering little forms. If a bird has food in abundance, it little fears the cold. I have kept parrakeets out through the blizzards and storms of a severe winter, seeing them play and frolic in the snow as if their natural home were an arctic tundra, instead of a tropical forest.

A friend of birds once planted many sprouts of wild honeysuckle about his porch, and the following summer two pairs of hummingbirds built their nests in near-by apple trees; he transplanted quantities of living woodbine to the garden fences, and when the robins returned in the spring, after having remained late the previous autumn feeding on the succulent bunches of berries, no fewer than ten pairs nested on and about the porch and yard.

So my text of this, as of many other weeks is,— study the food habits of the birds and stock your waste places with their favourite berry or vine. Your labour will be repaid a hundredfold in song and in the society of the little winged comrades.

> Worn is the winter rug of white,
> And in the snow-bare spots once more,
> Glimpses of faint green grass in sight,—
> Spring's footprints on the floor.
> Spring here—by what magician's touch?
> 'Twas winter scarce an hour ago.
> And yet I should have guessed as much,—
>   Those footprints in the snow!
>   FRANK DEMPSTER SHERMAN.

DWELLERS IN THE DUST

TO many of us the differences between a reptile and a batrachian are unknown. Even if we have learned that these interesting creatures are well worth studying and that they possess few or none of the unpleasant characteristics usually attributed to them, still we are apt to speak of having seen a lizard in the water at the pond's edge, or of having heard a reptile croaking near the march. To avoid such mistakes, one need only remember that reptiles are covered with scales and that batrachians have smooth skins.

Our walks will become more and more interesting as we spread our interest over a wider field, not confining our observations to birds and mammals alone, but including members of the two equally distinctive classes of animals mentioned above. The batrachians, in the northeastern part of our country, include the salamanders and newts, the frogs and toads, while as reptiles we number lizards, turtles, and snakes.

Lizards are creatures of the tropics and only two small species are found in our vicinity, and these occur but rarely. Snakes, however, are more abundant, and, besides the rare poisonous copperhead and rattlesnake, careful search will reveal a dozen harmless species, the commonest, of course, being the garter snake and its near relative the ribbon snake.

About this time of the year snakes begin to feel the thawing effect of the sun's rays and to stir in their long winter hibernation. Sometimes we will come upon a ball of six or eight intertwined snakes, which, if they are still frozen up, will lie motionless upon the ground. But when spring finally unclasps the seal which has been put upon tree and ground, these reptiles stretch themselves full length upon some exposed stone, where they lie basking in the sun.

The process of shedding the skin soon begins; getting clear of the head part, eye-scales and all, the serpent slowly wriggles its way forward, escaping from the old skin as a finger is drawn from a glove. At last it crawls away, bright and shining in its new scaly coat, leaving behind it a spectral likeness of itself, which slowly sinks and disintegrates amid the dead leaves and moss, or, later in the year, it may perhaps be discovered by some crested flycatcher and carried off to be added to its nesting material.

When the broods of twenty to thirty young garter snakes start out in life to hunt for themselves, then woe to the earthworms, for it is upon them that the little serpents chiefly feed.

Six or seven of our native species of snakes lay eggs, usually depositing them under the bark of rotten logs, or in similar places, where they are left to hatch by the heat of the sun or by that of the decaying vegetation. It is interesting to gather these leathery shelled eggs and watch them hatch, and it is surprising how similar to each other some of the various species are when they emerge from the shell.

APRIL

SPRING SONGSTERS

EARLY April sees the last contest which winter wages for supremacy, and often it is a half-hearted attempt; but after the army of the North has retreated, with its icicles and snowdrifts, spring seems dazed for a while. Victory has been dearly bought, and April is the season when, for a time, the trees and insects hang fire—paralysed—while the chill is thawing from their marrow. Our northern visitors of the bird world slip quietly away. There is no great gathering of clans like that of the tree swallows in the fall, but silently, one by one, they depart, following the last moan of the north wind, covering winter's disordered retreat with warbles and songs.

One evening we notice the juncos and tree sparrows in the tangled, frost-burned stubble, and the next day, although our eye catches glints of white from sparrow tails, it is from vesper finches, not from juncos, and the weed spray which a few hours before bent beneath a white-throat's weight, now vibrates with the energy which a field sparrow puts into his song. Field and chipping sparrows, which now come in numbers, are somewhat alike, but by their beaks and songs you may know them. The mandibles of the former are flesh-coloured, those of the latter black. The sharp *chip! chip!* is characteristic of the "chippy," but the sweet, dripping song of the field sparrow is charming. No elaborate performance this, but a succession of sweet, high notes, accelerating toward the end, like a coin of silver settling to rest on a marble table—a simple, chaste vespers which rises to the setting sun and endears the little brown singer to us.

We may learn much by studying these homely little frequenters of our orchards and pastures; each has a hundred secrets which await patient and careful watching by their human lovers. In the chipping sparrow we may notice a hint of the spring change of dress which warblers and tanagers carry to such an extreme. When he left us in the fall he wore a dull-streaked cap, but now he comes from the South attired in a smart headcovering of bright chestnut. Poor little fellow, this is the very best he can do in the way of especial ornament to bewitch his lady love, but it suffices. Can the peacock's train do more?

This is the time to watch for the lines of ducks crossing the sky, and be ready to find black ducks in the oddest places—even in insignificant rain pools deep in the woods. In the early spring the great flocks of grackles and redwings return, among the first to arrive as they were the last to leave for the South.

Before the last fox sparrow goes, the hermit

thrush comes, and these birds, alike in certain superficialities, but so actually unrelated, for a time seek their food in the same grove.

The hardier of the warblers pass us in April, stopping a few days before continuing to the northward. We should make haste to identify them and to learn all we can of their notes and habits, not only because of the short stay which most of them make, but on account of the vast assemblage of warbler species already on the move in the Southern States, which soon, in panoply of rainbow hues, will crowd our groves and wear thin the warbler pages of our bird books.

These April days we are sure to see flocks of myrtle, or yellow-rumped warblers, and yellow palm warblers in their olive-green coats and chestnut caps. The black-and-white creeper will always show himself true to his name—a creeping bundle of black and white streaks. When we hear of the parula warbler or of the Cape May warbler we get no idea of the appearance of the bird, but when we know that the black-throated green warblers begin to appear in April, the first good view of one of this species will proclaim him as such.

We have marked the fox sparrow as being a great scratcher among dead leaves. His habit is continued in the spring by the towhee, or chewink, who uses the same methods, throwing both feet backward simultaneously. The ordinary call note of this bird is a good example of how difficult it is to translate bird songs into human words. Listen to the quick, double note coming from the underbrush. Now he says *"towhee'!"* the next time *"chewink'!"* You may change about at will, and the notes will always correspond. Whatever is in our mind at the instant, that will seem to be what the bird says. This should warn us of the danger of reading our thoughts and theories too much into the minds and actions of birds. Their mental processes, in many ways, correspond to ours. When a bird expresses fear, hate, bravery, pain or pleasure, we can sympathise thoroughly with it, but in studying their more complex actions we should endeavour to exclude the thousand and one human attributes with which we are prone to colour the bird's mental environment.

John Burroughs has rendered the song of the black-throated green warbler in an inimitable way, as follows: "—— ——V——!" When we have once heard the bird we will instantly recognise the aptness of these symbolic lines. The least flycatcher, called *minimus* by the scientists, well deserves his name, for of all those members of his family which make their home with us, he is the smallest. These miniature flycatchers have a way of hunting which is all their own. They sit perched on some exposed twig or branch, motionless until some small insect flies in sight. Then they will launch out into the air, and, catching the insect with a snap of their beaks, fly back to the same perch. They are garbed in subdued grays, olives, and yellows. The least flycatcher has another name which at once distinguishes him —chebec'. As he sits on a limb, his whole body trembles when he jerks out these syllables, and his tail snaps as if it played some important part in the mechanism of his vocal effort.

When you are picking cowslips and hepaticas early in the month, keep a lookout for the first barn swallow. Nothing gives us such an impression of the independence and individuality of birds as when a solitary member of some species arrives days before others of his kind. One fork-tailed beauty of last year's nest above the hay-mow may hawk about for insects day after day alone, before he is joined by other swallows. Did he spend the winter by himself, or did the *heim-weh* smite his heart more sorely and bring him irresistibly to the loved nest in the rafters? This love of home, which is so striking an attribute of birds, is a wonderfully beautiful thing. It brings the oriole back to the branch where still swings her exquisite purse-shaped home of last summer; it leads each pair of fishhawks to their particular cartload of sticks, to which a few more must be added each year; it hastens the wing beats of the sea-swallows northward to the beach which, ten months ago, was flecked with their eggs—the shifting grains of sand their only nest.

This love of home, of birthplace, bridges over a thousand physical differences between these feathered creatures and ourselves. We forget their expressionless masks of horn, their feathered fingers, their scaly toes, and looking deep into their clear, bright eyes, we know and feel a kinship, a sympathy of spirit, which binds us all together, and we are glad.

> Yet these sweet sounds of the early season,
> And these fair sights of its sunny days,
> Are only sweet when we fondly listen,
> And only fair when we fondly gaze.
>
> There is no glory in star or blossom
> Till looked upon by a loving eye;
> There is no fragrance in April breezes
> Till breathed with joy as they wander by.
> WILLIAM CULLEN BRYANT.

THE SIMPLE ART OF SAPSUCKING

THE yellow-bellied sapsucker is, at this time of year, one of our most abundant woodpeckers, and in its life we have an excellent example of that individuality which is ever cropping out in Nature—the trial and acceptance of life under new conditions.

In the spring we tap the sugar maples, and gather great pailfuls of the sap as it rises from its winter resting-place in the roots, and the sapsucker likes to steal from our pails or to tap the trees for himself. But throughout part of the year he is satisfied with an insect diet and chooses the time when the sap begins to flow downward in the autumn for committing his most serious depredations upon the tree. It was formerly thought that this bird, like its near relatives, the downy and hairy woodpeckers, was forever boring for insects; but when we examine the regularity and symmetry of the arrangement of its holes, we realise that they are for a very different purpose than the exposing of an occasional grub.

Besides drinking the sap from the holes, this bird extracts a quantity of the tender inner bark of the tree, and when a tree has been encircled for several feet up and down its trunk by these

numerous little sap wells, the effect becomes apparent in the lessened circulation of the liquid
blood of the tree; and before long, death is certain
to ensue. So the work of the sapsucker is injurious, while the grub-seeking woodpeckers confer
only good upon the trees they frequent.

And how pitiful is the downfall of a doomed
tree! Hardly has its vitality been lessened an
appreciable amount, when somehow the word is
passed to the insect hordes who hover about in
waiting, as wolves hang upon the outskirts of a
herd of buffalo. In the spring, when the topmost
branches have received a little less than their
wonted amount of wholesome sap and the leaves
are less vigorous, the caterpillars and twig-
girdlers attack at once. Ichneumen flies and boring beetles seem to know by signs invisible to us
that here is opportunity. Then in the fall come
again the sapsuckers to the tree, remorselessly
driving hole after hole through the still untouched
segments of its circle of life. When the last sap-
channel is pierced and no more can pass to the
roots, the tree stands helpless, waiting for the
end. Swiftly come frost and rain, and when the
April suns again quicken all the surrounding
vegetation into vigorous life, the victim of the
sapsuckers stands lifeless, its branches reaching
hopelessly upward, a naked mockery amid the
warm green foliage around. Insects and fungi
and lightning now set to work unhindered, and

the tree falls at last,—dust to dust—ashes to ashes.

A sapsucker has been seen in early morning to sink forty or fifty wells into the bark of a mountain ash tree, and then to spend the rest of the day in sidling from one to another, taking a sip here and a drink there, gradually becoming more and more lethargic and drowsy, as if the sap actually produced some narcotic or intoxicating effect. Strong indeed is the contrast between such a picture and the same bird in the early spring,— then full of life and vigour, drawing musical reverberations from some resonant hollow limb.

Like other idlers, the sapsucker in its deeds of gluttony and harm brings, if anything, more injury to others than to itself. The farmers well know its depredations and detest it accordingly, but unfortunately they are not ornithologists, and a peckerwood is a peckerwood to them; and so while the poor downy, the red-head, and the hairy woodpeckers are seen busily at work cutting the life threads of the injurious borer larvæ, the farmer, thinking of his dying trees, slays them all without mercy or distinction. The sapsucker is never as confiding as the downy, and from a safe distance sees others murdered for sins which are his alone.

But we must give sapsucker his due and admit that he devours many hundreds of insects throughout the year, and though we mourn the

death of an occasional tree, we cannot but admire
his new venture in life,—his cunning in choosing
only the dessert served at the woodpeckers'
feasts,—the sweets which flow at the tap of a
beak, leaving to his fellows the labour of searching and drilling deep for more substantial courses.

WILD WINGS

THE ides of March see the woodcock back in its northern home, and in early April it prepares for nesting. The question of the nest itself is a very simple matter, being only a cavity, formed by the pressure of the mother's body, among the moss and dead leaves. The formalities of courtship are, however, quite another thing, and the execution of interesting aerial dances entails much effort and time.

It is in the dusk of evening that the male woodcock begins his song,—plaintive notes uttered at regular intervals, and sounding like *peent! peent!* Then without warning he launches himself on a sharply ascending spiral, his wings whistling through the gloom. Higher and higher he goes, balances a moment, and finally descends abruptly, with zigzag rushes, wings and voice both aiding each other in producing the sounds, to which, let us suppose, his prospective mate listens with ecstasy. It is a weird performance, repeated again and again during the same evening.

So pronounced and loud is the whistling of the wings that we wonder how it can be produced by ordinary feathers. The three outer primaries of the wing, which in most birds are usually like the others, in the woodcock are very stiff, and the vanes are so narrow that when the wing is spread there is a wide space between each one. When the wing beats the air rapidly, the wind rushes through these feather slits,—and we have the accompaniment of the love-song explained.

The feather-covered arms and hands of birds are full of interest; and after studying the wing of a chicken which has been plucked for the table, we shall realise how wonderful a transformation has taken place through the millions of years past. Only three stubby fingers are left and these are stiff and almost immovable, but the rest of the forearm is very like that of our own arm.

See how many facts we can accumulate about wings, by giving special attention to them, when watching birds fly across the sky. How easy it is to identify the steady beats of a crow, or the more rapid strokes of a duck; how distinctive is the frequent looping flight of a goldfinch, or the longer, more direct swings of a woodpecker!

Hardly any two birds have wings exactly similar in shape, every wing being exquisitely adapted to its owner's needs. The gull soars or flaps slowly on his long, narrow, tireless pinions, while the quail rises suddenly before us on short, rounded wings, which carry it like a rocket for a short distance, when it settles quickly to earth again. The gull would fare ill were it compelled to traverse the ocean with such brief spurts of speed, while, on the other hand, the last bob-white would shortly vanish, could it escape from fox or weasel only with the slow flight of a gull. How splendidly the sickle wings of a swift enable it to turn and twist, bat-like, in its pursuit of insects!

You may be able to identify any bird near your home, you may know its nest and eggs, its song and its young; but begin at the beginning again and watch their wings and their feet and their bills and you will find that there are new and wonderful truths at your very doorstep. Try bringing home from your walk a list of bill-uses or feet-functions. Remember that a familiar object, looked at from a new point of view, will take to itself unthought-of significance.

Whither midst falling dew,
　While glow the heavens with the last steps of day,
Far, through their rosy depths, dost thou pursue
　Thy solitary way?
WILLIAM CULLEN BRYANT.

THE BIRDS IN THE MOON

THE lover of birds who has spent the day in the field puts away his glasses at nightfall, looking forward to a walk after dark only as a chance to hear the call of nocturnal birds or to catch the whirr of a passing wing. But some bright moonlight night in early May, or again in mid September, unsheath your glasses and tie them, telescope-fashion, to a window-ledge or railing. Seat yourself in an easy position and focus on the moon. Shut out all earthly scenes from your mind and imagine yourself wandering amid those arid wastes. What a scene of cosmic desolation! What vast deserts, and gaping craters of barren rock! The cold, steel-white planet seems of all things most typical of death.

But those specks passing across its surface? At first you imagine they are motes clogging the delicate blood-vessels of the retina; then you wonder if a distant host of falling meteors could have passed. Soon a larger, nearer mote appears; the moon and its craters are forgotten and with a thrill of delight you realise that they are birds—living, flying birds—of all earthly things typical of the most vital life! Migration is at its height, the chirps and twitters which come from the surrounding darkness are tantalising hints telling of the passing legions. Thousands and thousands of birds are every night pouring north-ward in a swift, invisible, aerial stream.

As a projecting pebble in mid-stream blurs the transparent water with a myriad bubbles, so the narrow path of moon-rays, which our glass re-veals, cuts a swath of visibility straight through the host of birds to our eager eyes. How we hate to lose an instant's opportunity! Even a wink may allow a familiar form to pass unseen. If we can use a small telescope, the field of view is much enlarged. Now and then we recognise the flight of some particular species,—the swinging loop of a woodpecker or goldfinch, or the flutter of a sandpiper.

It has been computed that these birds some-times fly as much as a mile or more above the sur-face of the earth, and when we think of the tiny, fluttering things at this terrible height, it takes our breath away. What a panorama of dark earth and glistening river and ocean must be spread out beneath them! How the big moon must glow in that rarefied air! How diminutive and puerile must seem the houses and cities of human fashioning!

The instinct of migration is one of the most wonderful in the world. A young bob-white and a bobolink are hatched in the same New England field. The former grows up and during the fall and winter forms one of the covey which is content to wander a mile or two, here and there, in search of good feeding grounds. Hardly has the bobolink donned his first full dress before an irresistible impulse seizes him. One night he rises up and up, ever higher on fluttering wings, sets his course southward, gives you a glimpse of him across the moon, and keeps on through Virginia to Florida, across seas, over tropical islands, far into South America, never content until he has put the great Amazon between him and his far distant birthplace.

He who, from zone to zone,
  Guides through the boundless sky thy certain flight,
In the long way that I must tread alone,
  Will lead my steps aright.
                    WILLIAM CULLEN BRYANT.

MAY

THE HIGH TIDE OF BIRD LIFE

FOR abundance and for perfection of song and plumage, of the whole year, May is the month of birds. Insects appear slowly in the spring and are numerous all summer; squirrels and mice are more or less in evidence during all the twelve months; reptiles unearth themselves at the approach of the warm weather, and may be found living their slow, sluggish life until late in the fall. In eggs, cocoons, discarded bird's-nests, in earthen burrows, or in the mud at the bottom of pond or stream, all these creatures have spent the winter near where we find them in the spring. But birds are like creatures of another world; and, although in every summer's walk we may see turtles, birds, butterflies, and chipmunks, all interweaving their life paths across one another's haunts, yet the power of extended flight and the wonderful habit of continental migration set birds apart from all other living creatures. A bird during its lifetime has almost twice the conscious existence of, say, a snake or any hibernating mammal. And now in early May, when the creatures of the woods and fields have only recently opened their sleepy eyes and stretched their thin forms, there comes the great world-wide army of the birds, whose bright eyes peer at us from tree, thicket, and field, whose brilliant feathers and sweet songs bring summer with a leap—the height of the grand symphony, of which the vernal peeping of the frogs and the squirrels' chatter were only the first notes of the prelude.

Tantalus-like is the condition of the amateur bird-lover, who, book in hand, vainly endeavours to identify the countless beautiful forms which appear in such vast numbers, linger a few days and then disappear, passing on to the northward, but leaving behind a goodly assemblage which spends the summer and gives abundant opportunity for study during the succeeding months. In May it is the migrants which we should watch, and listen to, and "ogle" with our opera glasses. Like many other evanescent things, those birds which have made their winter home in Central America—land yet beyond our travels—and which use our groves merely as half-way houses on their journey to the land of their birth, the balsams of Quebec, or the unknown wastes of Labrador, seem most precious, most worthy at this time of our closest observation.

More confusing—albeit the more delightful— is a season when continued cold weather and chilly rains hold back all but the hardiest birds, until— like the dammed-up piles of logs trembling with the spring freshets—the tropic winds carry all before them, and all at once winter birds which have sojourned only a few miles south of us, summer residents which should have appeared weeks ago, together with the great host of Canadian and other nesters of the north, appear within a few days' time.

A backward season brings strangers into close company for a while. A white-throat sings his clear song of the North, and a moment later is answered by an oriole's melody, or the sweet tones of a rose-breasted grosbeak—the latter one of those rarely favoured birds, exquisite in both plumage and song.

The glories of our May bird life are the wood warblers, and innumerable they must seem to one who is just beginning his studies; indeed, there are over seventy species that find their way into the United States. Many are named from the distribution of colour upon their plumage—the blue-winged yellow, the black-throated blue, chestnut-sided, bay-breasted, and black poll. Perhaps the two most beautiful—most reflective of bright tropical skies and flowers—are the magnolia and the blackburnian. The first fairly dazzles us with its bluish crown, white and black face, black and olive-green back, white marked wings and tail, yellow throat and rump, and strongly streaked breast. The blackburnian is an exquisite little fellow, marked with white and black, but with the crown several patches on the face, the throat and breast of a rich warm orange that glows amid the green foliage like a living coal of fire. The black poll warbler is an easy bird to identify; but do not expect to recognise it when it returns from the North in the fall. Its black crown has disappeared, and in general it looks like a different bird.

At the present time when the dogwood blossoms are in their full perfection, and the branches and twigs of the trees are not yet hidden, but their outlines only softened by the light, feathery foliage, the tanagers and orioles have their day. Nesting cares have not yet made them fearful of showing their bright plumage, and scores of the scarlet and orange forms play among the branches.

The flycatchers and vireos now appear in force —little hunters of insects clad in leafy greens and browns, with now and then a touch of brightness —as in the yellow-throated vireo or in the crest of the kingbird.

The lesser sandpipers, both the spotted and the solitary, teeter along the brooks and ponds, and probe the shallows for tiny worms. Near the woody streams the so-called water thrushes spring up before us. Strange birds these, in appearance like thrushes, in their haunts and in their teetering motion like sandpipers, but in reality belonging to the same family as the tree-loving wood warblers. A problem not yet solved by ornithologists is: what was the mode of life of the ancestor of the many warblers? Did he cling to and creep along the bark, as the black-and-white warbler, or feed from the ground or the thicket as does the worm-eating? Did he snatch flies on the wing as the necklaced Canadian warbler, or glean from the brook's edge as our water thrush? The struggle for existence has not been absent from the lives of these light-hearted little fellows, and they have had to be jack-of-all-trades in their search for food.

The gnats and other flying insects have indeed to take many chances when they slip from their cocoons and dance up and down in the warm sunlight! Lucky for their race that there are millions instead of thousands of them; for now the swifts and great numbers of tree and barn swallows spend the livelong day in swooping after the unfortunate gauzy-winged motes, which have risen above the toad's maw upon land, and beyond the reach of the trout's leap over the water.

It would take an article as long as this simply to mention hardly more than the names of the birds that we may observe during a walk in May; and with bird book and glasses we must see for ourselves the bobolinks in the broad meadows, the cowbirds and rusty blackbirds, and, pushing through the lady-slipper marshes, we may surprise the solitary great blue and the little green herons at their silent fishing.

No matter how late the spring may be, the great

migration host will reach its height from the tenth to the fifteenth of the month. From this until June first, migrants will be passing, but in fewer and fewer numbers, until the balance comes to rest again, and we may cease from the strenuous labours of the last few weeks, confident that those birds that remain will be the builders of the nests near our homes—nests that they know so well how to hide. Even before the last day of May passes, we see many young birds on their first weak-winged flights, such as bluebirds and robins; but June is the great month of bird homes, as to May belong the migrants.

> Robins and mocking birds that all day long
> Athwart straight sunshine weave cross-threads of song.
> SIDNEY LANIER.

ANIMAL FASHIONS

WARM spring days bring other changes than thawing snowbanks and the swelling buds and leaves, which seem to grow almost visibly. It is surprising how many of the wild folk meet the spring with changed appearance—beautiful, fantastic or ugly to us; all, perhaps, beautiful to them and to their mates.

As a rule we find the conditions which exist among ourselves reversed among the animals; the male "blossoms forth like the rose," while the female's sombre winter fur or feathers are reduplicated only by a thinner coat for summer. The "spring opening" of the great classes of birds and animals is none the less interesting because its styles are not set by Parisian modistes.

The most gorgeous display of all is to be found among the birds, the peacock leading in conspicuousness and self-consciousness. What a contrast to the dull earthy-hued little hen, for whose slightest favour he neglects food to raise his Argus-eyed fan, clattering his quill castanets and screaming challenges to his rivals! He will even fight bloody battles with invading suitors; and, after all, failure may be the result. Imagine the feelings of two superb birds fighting over a winsome browny, to see her—as I have done—walk off with a spurless, half-plumaged young cock!

The males of many birds, such as the scarlet tanager and the indigo bunting, assume during the winter the sombre green or brown hue of the female, changing in spring to a glorious scarlet and black, or to an exquisite indigo colour respectively. Not only do most of the females of the feathered world retain their dull coats throughout the year, but some deface even this to form feather beds for the precious eggs and nestlings, to protect which bright colours must be entirely foregone.

The spring is the time when decorations are seen at their best. The snowy egret trails his filmy cloud of plumes, putting to shame the stiff millinery bunches of similar feathers torn from his murdered brethren. Even the awkward and querulous night heron exhibits a long curling plume or two. And what a strange criterion of beauty a female white pelican must have! To be sure, the graceful crest which Sir Pelican erects is beautiful, but that huge, horny "keel" or "sight" on his bill! What use can it subserve, æsthetic or otherwise? One would think that such a structure growing so near his eyes, and day by day becoming taller, must occupy much of his attention.

The sheldrake ducks also have a fleshy growth on the bill. A turkey gobbler, when his vernal wedding dress is complete, is indeed a remarkable sight. The mass of wattles, usually so gray and shrunken, is now of most vivid hues—scarlet, blue, vermilion, green,—the fleshy tassels and swollen knobs making him a most extraordinary creature.

Birds are noted for taking exquisite care of their plumage, and if the feathers become at all dingy or unkempt, we know the bird is in bad health.

What a time the deer and the bears, the squirrels and the mice, have when changing their dress! Rags and tatters; tatters and rags! One can grasp a handful of hair on the flank of a caribou or elk in a zoological park, and the whole will come out like thistledown; while underneath is seen the sleek, short summer coat. A bear will sometimes carry a few locks of the long, brown winter fur for months after the clean black hairs of the summer's coat are grown. What a boon to human tailors such an opportunity would be—to ordain that Mr. X. must wear the faded collar or vest of his old suit until bills are paid!

It is a poor substance, indeed, which, when cast aside, is not available for some secondary use in Nature's realm; and the hairs that fall from animals are not all left to return unused to their original elements. The sharp eyes of birds spy them out, and thus the lining to many a nest is furnished. I knew of one feathered seeker of cast-off clothing which met disaster through trying to get a supply at first hand—a sparrow was found dead, tangled in the hairs of a pony's tail. The chickadee often lights on the backs of domestic cattle and plucks out hair with which to line some snug cavity near by for his nest. Before the cattle came his ancestors were undoubtedly in the habit of helping themselves from the deer's stock of "ole clo's," as they have been observed getting their building material from the deer in zoological parks.

Of course the hair of deer and similar animals falls out with the motions of the creatures, or is brushed out by bushes and twigs; but we must hope that the shedding place of a porcupine is at a distance from his customary haunts; it would be so uncomfortable to run across a shred of one's old clothes—if one were a porcupine!

The skin of birds and animals wears away in small flakes, but when a reptile changes to a new suit of clothes, the old is shed almost entire. A frog after shedding its skin will very often turn round and swallow it, establishing the frog maxim "every frog his own old clothes bag!"

Birds, which exhibit so many idiosyncrasies, appear again as utilizers of old clothes; although when a crested flycatcher weaves a long snakeskin into the fabric of its nest, it seems more from the standpoint of a curio collector—as some people delight in old worn brass and blue china! There is another if less artistic theory for this peculiarity of the crested flycatcher. The skin of a

snake—a perfect ghost in its completeness—
would make a splendid "bogie." We can see that
it might, indeed, be useful in such a way, as in
frightening marauding crows, who approach with
cannibalistic intentions upon eggs or young.
Thus the skin would correspond in function to
the rows of dummy wooden guns, which make a
weak fort appear all but invincible.

POLLIWOG PROBLEMS

THE ancient Phœnicians, Egyptians, Hindus, Japanese, and Greeks all shared the belief that the whole world was hatched from an egg made by the Creator. This idea of development is at least true in the case of every living thing upon the earth to-day; every plant springs from its seed, every animal from its egg. And still another sweeping, all-inclusive statement may be made,—every seed or egg at first consists of but one cell, and by the division of this into many cells, the lichen, violet, tree, worm, crab, butterfly, fish, frog, or other higher creature is formed. A little embryology will give a new impetus to our studies, whether we watch the unfolding leaves of a sunflower, a caterpillar emerging from its egg, or a chick breaking through its shell.

The very simplest and best way to begin this study is to go to the nearest pond, where the frogs have been croaking in the evenings. A search among the dead leaves and water-soaked sticks will reveal a long string of black beads. These are the eggs of the toad; if, however, the beads are not in strings, but in irregular masses, then they are frogs' eggs. In any case take home a tumblerful, place a few, together with the thick, transparent gelatine, in which they are encased,

110

in a saucer, and examine them carefully under
a good magnifying glass, or, better still, through
a low-power microscope lens.

You will notice that the tiny spheres are not
uniformly coloured but that half is whitish. If
the eggs have been recently laid the surface will
be smooth and unmarked, but have patience and
watch them for as long a time as you can spare.
Whenever I can get a batch of such eggs, I never
grudge a whole day spent in observing them, for
it is seldom that the mysterious processes of life
are so readily watched and followed.

Keep your eye fixed on the little black and white
ball of jelly and before long, gradually and yet
with never a halt, a tiny furrow makes its way
across the surface, dividing the egg into equal
halves. When it completely encircles the sphere
you may know that you have seen one of the
greatest wonders of the world. The egg which
consisted of but one cell is now divided into two
exactly equal parts, of the deepest significance.
Of the latter truth we may judge from the fact
that if one of those cells should be injured, only
one-half a polliwog would result,—either a head
or a tail half.

Before long the unseen hand of life ploughs another furrow across the egg, and we have now
four cells. These divide into eight, sixteen, and so
on far beyond human powers of numeration, until
the beginnings of all the organs of the tadpole

are formed. While we cannot, of course, follow this development, we can look at our egg every day and at last see the little *wiggle heads* or polliwogs (from *pol* and *wiggle*) emerge.

In a few days they develop a fin around the tail, and from now on it is an easy matter to watch the daily growth. There is no greater miracle in the world than to see one of these aquatic, water-breathing, limbless creatures transform before your eyes into a terrestrial, four-legged frog or toad, breathing air like ourselves. The humble polliwog in its development is significant of far more marvellous facts than the caterpillar changing into the butterfly, embodying as it does the deepest poetry and romance of evolution.

> Blue dusk, that brings the dewy hours,
> Brings thee, of graceless form in sooth.
>
> EDGAR FAWCETT.

INSECT PIRATES AND SUBMARINES

FAR out on the ocean, when the vessel is laboriously making her way through the troughs and over the crests of the great waves, little birds, black save for a patch of white on the lower back, are a common sight, flying with quick irregular wing-beats, close to the surface of the troubled waters. When they spy some edible bit floating beneath them, down they drop until their tiny webbed feet just rest upon the water. Then, snatching up the titbit, half-flying, they patter along the surface of the water, just missing being engulfed by each oncoming wave. Thus they have come to be named petrels—little Peters—because they seem to walk upon the water. Without aid from the wings, however, they would soon be immersed, so the walking is only an illusion.

But in our smallest ponds and brooks we may see this miracle taking place almost daily, the feat being accomplished by a very interesting little assemblage of insects, commonly called water skaters or striders. Let us place our eyes as near as possible to the surface of the water and watch the little creatures darting here and there.

We see that they progress securely on the top

113

of the water, resting upon it as if it were a sheet of ice. Their feet are so adapted that the water only dimples beneath their slight weight, the extent of the depression not being visible to the eye, but clearly outlined in the shadows upon the bottom. In an eddy of air a tiny fly is caught and whirled upon the water, where it struggles vigorously, striving to lift its wings clear of the surface. In an instant the water strider—pirate of the pond that he is—reaches forward his crooked fore legs, and here endeth the career of the unfortunate fly.

In the air, in the earth, and below the surface of the water are hundreds of living creatures, but the water striders and their near relatives are unique. No other group shares their power of actually walking, or rather pushing themselves, upon the surface of the water. They have a little piece of the world all to themselves. Yet, although three fifths of the earth's surface consists of water, this group of insects is a small one. A very few, however, are found out upon the ocean, where the tiny creatures row themselves cheerfully along. It is thought that they attach their eggs to the floating saragassum seaweed. If only we knew the whole life of one of these ocean water striders and all the strange sights it must see, a fairy story indeed would be unfolded to us.

However, all the Lilliputian craft of our brooks are not galleys; there are submarines, which, in excellence of action and control, put to shame all human efforts along the same line. These are the water boatmen, stout boat-shaped insects whose hind legs are long, projecting outward like the oars of a rowboat. They feather their oars, too, or rather the oars are feathered for them, a fringe of long hairs growing out on each side of the blade. Some of the boatmen swim upside down, and these have the back keeled instead of the breast. Like real submarine boats, these insects have to come up for air occasionally; and, again like similar craft of human handiwork, their principal mission in life seems to be warfare upon the weaker creatures about them.

Upon their bodies are many short hairs that have the power of enclosing and retaining a good-sized bubble of air. Thus the little boatman is well supplied for each submarine trip, and he does not have to return to the surface until all this storage air has been exhausted. In perfectly pure water, however, these boatmen can remain almost indefinitely below the surface, although it is not known how they obtain from the water the oxygen which they usually take from the air.

All of these skaters and boatmen thrive in small aquariums, and if given pieces of scraped meat will live in perfect health. Here is an alluring opportunity for anyone to add to our knowledge of insect life; for the most recent scientific books admit that we do not yet know the complete life history of even one of these little brothers of the pond.

> Clear and cool, clear and cool,
> By laughing shallow, and dreaming pool;
> Cool and clear, cool and clear,
> By shining shingle, and foaming weir.
>
>   CHARLES KINGSLEY.

THE VICTORY OF THE NIGHTHAWK

THE time is not far distant when the bottom of the sea will be the only place where primeval wildness will not have been defiled or destroyed by man. He may sail his ships above, he may peer downward, even dare to descend a few feet in a suit of rubber or a submarine boat, or he may scratch a tiny furrow for a few yards with a dredge: but that is all.

When that time comes, the animals and birds which survive will be only those which have found a way to adapt themselves to man's encroaching, all-pervading civilisation. The time was when our far-distant ancestors had, year in and year out, to fight for very existence against the wild creatures about them. They then gained the upper hand, and from that time to the present the only question has been, how long the wild creatures of the earth could hold out.

The wolf, the bison, the beaver fought the battle out at once to all but the bitter end. The crow, the muskrat, the fox have more than held their own, by reason of cunning, hiding or quickness of sight; but they cannot hope for this to last. The English sparrow has won by sheer audacity; but most to be admired are those creatures which have so changed their habits that

117

some product of man's invention serves them as well as did their former wilderness home. The eave swallow and barn swallow and the chimney swift all belie their names in the few wild haunts still uninvaded by man. The first two were originally cliff and bank haunters, and the latter's home was a lightning-hollowed tree.

But the nighthawks which soar and boom above our city streets, whence come they? Do they make daily pilgrimages from distant woods? The city furnishes no forest floor on which they may lay their eggs. Let us seek a wide expanse of flat roof, high above the noisy, crowded streets. Let it be one of those tar and pebble affairs, so unpleasant to walk upon, but so efficient in shedding water. If we are fortunate, as we walk slowly across the roof, a something, like a brownish bit of wind-blown rubbish, will roll and tumble ahead of us. It is a bird with a broken wing, we say. How did it ever get up here? We hasten forward to pick it up, when, with a last desperate flutter, it topples off the edge of the roof; but instead of falling helplessly to the street, the bird swings out above the house-tops, on the white-barred pinions of a nighthawk. Now mark the place where first we observed the bird, and approach it carefully, crawling on hands and knees. Otherwise we will very probably crush the two mottled bits of shell, so exactly like pebbles in external appearance, but sheltering two little warm, beating hearts.   Soon the shells will crack, and the young nighthawks will emerge,—tiny fluffs,—in colour the very essence of the scattered pebbles.

In the autumn they will all pass southward to the far distant tropics, and when spring again awakens, the instinct of migration will lead them, not to some mottled carpet of moss and rocks deep in the woods, but to the tarred roof of a house in the very heart of a great city.

JUNE

THE GALA DAYS OF BIRDS

MIGRATION is over, and the great influx of birds which last month filled every tree and bush is now distributed over field and wood, from our dooryard and lintel vine to the furthermost limits of northern exploration; birds, perhaps, having discovered the pole long years ago. Now every feather and plume is at its brightest and full development; for must not the fastidious females be sought and won?

And now the great struggle of the year is at hand, the supreme moment for which thousands of throats have been vibrating with whispered rehearsals of trills and songs, and for which the dangers that threaten the acquisition of bright colours and long, inconvenient plumes and ornaments have been patiently undergone. Now, if all goes well and his song is clear, if his crest and gorgeous splashes of tints and shades are fresh and shining with the gloss of health, then the feathered lover may hope, indeed, that the little brown mate may look with favour upon dance, song, or antic—and the home is become a reality. In some instances this home is for only one short season, when the two part, probably forever; but in other cases the choice is for life.

But if his rival is stronger, handsomer, and—victorious, what then? Alas, the song dies in his throat, plumes hang crestfallen, and the disconsolate creature must creep about through tangles and brush, watching from a distance the nest-building, the delights of home life which fate has forbidden. But the poor bachelor need not by any means lose hope; for on all sides dangers threaten his happy rival—cats, snakes, jays, hawks, owls, and boys. Hundreds of birds must pay for their victory with their lives, and then the once discarded suitors are quickly summoned by the widows; and these step-fathers, no whit chagrined at playing second fiddle, fill up the ranks, and work for the young birds as if they were their own offspring.

There is an unsolved mystery about the tragedies and comedies that go on every spring. Usually every female bird has several suitors, of which one is accepted. When the death of this mate occurs, within a day or two another is found; and this may be repeated a dozen times in succession. Not only this, but when a female bird is killed, her mate is generally able at once somewhere, somehow, to find another to take her place. Why these unmated males and females remain single until they are needed is something that has never been explained.

The theme of the courtship of birds is marvellously varied and comparatively little understood.

Who would think that when our bald eagle, of
national fame, seeks to win his mate, his ardour
takes the form of an undignified galloping dance,
round and round her from branch to branch!
Hardly less ridiculous—to our eyes—is the
elaborate performance of our most common woodpecker, the flicker, or high-hole. Two or three
male birds scrape and bow and pose and chatter
about the demure female, outrageously undignified as compared with their usual behaviour. They
do everything save twirl their black moustaches!

In the mating season some birds have beauties
which are ordinarily concealed. Such is the male
ruby-crowned kinglet, garbed in gray and green,
the two sexes identical, except for the scarlet
touch on the crown of the male, which, at courting
time, he raises and expands. Even the iris of
some birds changes and brightens in colour at the
breeding season; while in others there appear
about the base of the bill horny parts, which in a
month or two fall off. The scarlet coat of the
tanager is perhaps solely for attracting and holding the attention of the female, as before winter
every feather is shed, the new plumage being of
a dull green, like that of its mate and its young.

As mystery confronts us everywhere in nature,
so we confess ourselves baffled when we attempt
to explain the most wonderful of all the attributes
of bird courtship—song. Birds have notes to call
to one another, to warn of danger, to express

anger and fear; but the highest development of
their vocal efforts seems to be devoted to charming the females. If birds have a love of music,
then there must be a marvellous diversity of taste
among them, ranging all the way from the shrieking, strident screams of the parrots and macaws
to the tender pathos of the wood pewee and the
hermit thrush.

If birds have not some appreciation of sweet
sounds, then we must consider the many different
songs as mere by-products, excess of vitality
which expresses itself in results, in many cases,
strangely æsthetic and harmonious. A view mid-
way is indefinable as regards the boundaries
covered by each theory. How much of the peacock's train or of the thrush's song is appreciated
by the female? How much is by-product merely?

In these directions a great field lies open to the
student and lover of birds; but however we decide
for ourselves in regard to the exact meaning and
evolution of song, and what use it subserves
among the birds, we all admit the effect and pleasure it produces in ourselves. A world without the
song of birds is greatly lacking—such is a desert,
where even the harsh croak of a raven is melody.

Perhaps the reason why the songs of birds give
more lasting pleasure than many other things is
that sound is so wonderfully potent to recall days
and scenes of our past life. Like a sunset, the

vision that a certain song brings is different to each one of us.

To me, the lament of the wood pewee brings to mind deep, moist places in the Pennsylvania back-woods; the crescendo of the oven bird awakens memories of the oaks of the Orange mountains; when a loon or an olive-sided flycatcher or a white-throat calls, the lakes and forests of Nova Scotia come vividly to mind; the cry of a sea-swallow makes real again the white beaches of Virginia; to me a cardinal has in its song the feathery lagoons of Florida's Indian River, while the shriek of a macaw and its antithesis, the silvery, interlacing melodies of the solitaire, spell the farthest *barrancas* of Mexico, with the vultures ever circling overhead, and the smoke clouds of the volcano in the distance.

So sweet, so sweet the calling of the thrushes,
    The calling, cooing, wooing, everywhere;
So sweet the water's song through reeds and rushes,
    The plover's piping note, now here, now there.
                                    NORA PERRY.

TURTLE TRAITS

A TURTLE, waddling his solitary way along some watercourse, attracts little attention apart from that aroused by his clumsy, grotesque shape; yet few who look upon him are able to give offhand even a bare half-dozen facts about the humble creature. Could they give any information at all, it would probably be limited to two or three usages to which his body is put—such as soup, mandolin picks, and combs.

In the northeastern part of our own country we may look for no fewer than eight species of turtles which are semi-aquatic, living in or near ponds and streams, while another, the well-known box tortoise, confines its travels to the uplands and woods.

There are altogether about two hundred different kinds of turtles, and they live in all except the very cold countries of the world. Australia has the fewest and North and Central America the greatest number of species. Evolutionists can tell us little or nothing of the origin of these creatures, for as far back in geological ages as they are found fossil (a matter of a little over ten million years), all are true turtles, not half turtles and half something else. Crocodiles and alligators, with their hard leathery coats, come as near to them as do any living creatures, and when we see a huge snapping turtle come out of the water and walk about on land, we cannot fail to be reminded of the fellow with the armoured back.

Turtles are found on the sea and on land, the marine forms more properly deserving the name of turtles; tortoises being those living on land or in fresh water. We shall use the name turtle as significant of the whole group. The most natural method of classifying these creatures is by the way the head and neck are drawn back under the shell; whether the head is turned to one side, or drawn straight back, bending the neck into the letter S shape.

The skull of a turtle is massive, and some have thick, false roofs on top of the usual brain box.

The "house" or shell of a turtle is made up of separate pieces of bone, a central row along the back and others arranged around on both sides. These are really pieces of the skin of the back changed to bone. Our ribs are directly under the skin of the back, and if this skin should harden into a bone-like substance, the ribs would lie flat against it, and this is the case with the ribs of turtles. So when we marvel that the ribs of a turtle are on the outside of its body, a second thought will show us that this is just as true of us as it is of these reptiles.

This hardening of the skin has brought about some interesting changes in the body of the turtle.

In all the higher animals, from fishes up to man, a backbone is of the greatest importance not only in carrying the nerves and blood-vessels, but in supporting the entire body. In turtles alone, the string of vertebræ is unnecessary, the shell giving all the support needed. So, as Nature seldom allows unused tissues or organs to remain, these bones along the back become, in many species, reduced to a mere thread.

The pieces of bone or horn which go to make up the shell, although so different in appearance from the skin, yet have the same life-processes. Occasionally the shell moults or peels, the outer part coming off in great flakes. Each piece grows by the addition of rings of horn at the joints, and (like the rings of a tree) the age of turtles, except of very old ones, can be estimated by the number of circles of horn on each piece. The rings are very distinct in species which live in temperate climates. Here they are compelled to hibernate during the winter, and this cessation of growth marks the intervals between each ring. In tropical turtles the rings are either absent or indistinct. It is to this mode of growth that the spreading of the initials which are cut into the shell is due, just as letters carved on the trunks of trees in time broaden and bulge outward.

The shell has the power of regeneration, and when a portion is crushed or torn away the injured parts are gradually cast off, and from the

surrounding edges a new covering of horn grows
out. One third of the entire shell has been known
to be thus replaced.

Although so slow in their locomotion and
actions, turtles have well-developed senses. They
can see very distinctly, and the power of smell is
especially acute, certain turtles being very dis-
criminating in the matter of food. They are also
very sensitive to touch, and will react to the least
tap on their shells. Their hearing, however, is
more imperfect, but as during the mating season
they have tiny, piping voices, this sense must be
of some use.

Water tortoises can remain beneath the surface
for hours and even days at a time. In addition
to the lungs there are two small sacs near the tail
which allow the animal to use the oxygen in the
water as an aid to breathing.

All turtles lay eggs, the shells of which are white
and generally of a parchment-like character. They
are deposited in the ground or in the sand, and
hatch either by the warmth of the decaying vegetation or by the heat of the sun. In temperate
countries the eggs remain through the winter, and
the little turtles do not emerge until the spring.
The eggs of turtles are very good to eat, and the
oil contained in them is put to many uses. In all
the countries which they inhabit, young turtles
have a hard time of it; for thousands of them are
devoured by storks, alligators, and fishes. Even

old turtles have many enemies, not the least strange being jaguars, which watch for them, turn them on their backs with a flip of the paw, and eat them at leisure—on the half shell, as it were!

Leathery turtles—which live in the sea—have been reported weighing over a thousand pounds! This species is very rare, and a curious circumstance is that only very large adults and very small baby individuals have been seen, the turtles of all intermediate growths keeping in the deep ocean out of view.

Snapping turtles are among the fiercest creatures in the world. On leaving the egg their first instinct is to open their mouths and bite at something. They feed on almost anything, but when in captivity they sometimes refuse to eat, and have been known to go a year without food, showing no apparent ill effects. One method which they employ in capturing their food is interesting. A snapping turtle will lie quietly at the bottom of a pond or lake, looking like an old water-soaked log with a branch—its head and neck—at one end. From the tip of the tongue the creature extrudes two small filaments of a pinkish colour which wriggle about, bearing a perfect resemblance to the small round worms of which fishes are so fond. Attracted by these, fishes swim up to grasp the squirming objects and are engulfed by the cruel mouth of the angler. Certain marine turtles have long-fringed appendages on the head and neck, which, waving about, serve a similar purpose.

The edible terrapin has, in many places, become very rare; so that thousands of them are kept and bred in enclosed areas, or "crawls," as they are called. This species is noted for its curious disposition, and it is often captured by being attracted by some unusual sound.

The tortoise-shell of commerce is obtained from the shell of the hawksbill turtle, the plates of which, being very thin, are heated and welded together until of the required thickness. The age to which turtles live has often been exaggerated, but they are certainly the longest lived of all living creatures. Individuals from the Galapagos Island are estimated to be over four hundred years old. When, in a zoological garden, we see one of these creatures and study his aged, aged look, as he slowly and deliberately munches the cabbage which composes his food, we can well believe that such a being saw the light of day before Columbus made his memorable voyage.

> He's his own landlord, his own tenant; stay
> Long as he will, he dreads no Quarter Day.
> Himself he boards and lodges; both invites
> And feasts himself; sleeps with himself o'nights.
> He spares the upholsterer trouble to procure
> Chattels; himself is his own furniture,
> Knock when you will,—he's sure to be at home.
> CHARLES LAMB.

A HALF-HOUR IN A MARSH

THERE are little realms all around of which many of us know nothing. Take, for example, some marsh within a half-hour's trolley ride of any of our cities or towns. Select one where cat-tails and reeds abound. Mosquitoes and fear of malaria keep these places free from invasion by humankind; but if we select some windy day we may laugh them both to scorn, and we shall be well repaid for our trip. The birds frequenting these places are so seldom disturbed that they make only slight effort to conceal their nests, and we shall find plenty of the beautiful bird cradles rocking with every passing breeze.

A windy day will also reveal an interesting feature of the marsh. The soft, velvety grass, which abounds in such places, is so pliant and yielding that it responds to every breath, and each approaching wave of air is heralded by an advancing curl of the grass. At our feet these grass-waves intersect and recede, giving a weird sensation, as if the ground were moving, or as if we were walking on the water itself. Where the grass is longer, the record of some furious gale is permanently fixed—swaths and ripples seeming to roll onward, or to break into green foam. The simile of a "painted ocean" is perfectly carried

out. There is no other substance, not even sand,
which simulates more exactly the motions of water than this grass.

In the nearest clump of reeds we notice several
red-winged blackbirds, chattering nervously. A
magnificent male bird, black as night, and with
scarlet epaulets burning on his shoulders, swoops
at us, while his inconspicuous brownish consorts
vibrate above the reeds, some with grubs, some
empty mouthed. They are invariable indexes of
what is below them. We may say with perfect
assurance that in that patch of rushes are two
nests, one with young; beyond are three others,
all with eggs.

We find beautiful structures, firm and round,
woven of coarse grasses inside and dried reeds
without, hung between two or three supporting
stalks, or, if it is a fresh-water marsh, sheltered
by long, green fern fronds. The eggs are worthy
of their cradles—pearly white in colour, with
scrawls and blotches of dark purple at the larger
end—hieroglyphics which only the blackbirds can
translate.

In another nest we find newly hatched young,
looking like large strawberries, their little naked
bodies of a vivid orange colour, with scanty gray
tufts of down here and there. Not far away is a
nest, overflowing with five young birds ready to
fly, which scramble out at our approach and start
boldly off; but as their weak wings give out, they

soon come to grief. We catch one and find that it has most delicate colours, resembling its mother in being striped brown and black, although its breast and under parts are of an unusually beautiful tint—a kind of salmon pink. I never saw this shade elsewhere in Nature.

Blackbirds are social creatures, and where we find one nest, four or five others may be looked for near by. The red-winged blackbird is a mormon in very fact, and often a solitary male bird may be seen guarding a colony of three or four nests, each with an attending female. A sentiment of altruism seems indeed not unknown, as I have seen a female give a grub to one of a hungry nestful, before passing on to brood her own eggs, yet unhatched.

While looking for the blackbirds' nests we shall come across numerous round, or oval, masses of dried weeds and grass—mice homes we may think them; and the small, winding entrance concealed on one side tends to confirm this opinion. Several will be empty, but when in one our fingers touch six or eight tiny eggs, our mistake will be apparent. Long-billed marsh wrens are the architects, and so fond are they of building that frequently three or four unused nests are constructed before the little chocolate jewels are deposited.

If we sit quietly for a few moments, one of the owners, overcome by wren curiosity, will appear, clinging to a reed stalk and twitching his pert, upturned tail, the badge of his family. Soon he springs up into the air and, bubbling a jumble of liquid notes, sinks back into the recesses of the cat-tails. Another and another repeat this until the marsh rings with their little melodies.

If we seat ourselves and watch quietly we may possibly behold an episode that is not unusual. The joyous songs of the little wrens suddenly give place to cries of fear and anger; and this hubbub increases until at last we see a sinister ripple flowing through the reeds, marking the advancing head of a water snake.

The evil eyes of the serpent are bent upon the nearest nest, and toward it he makes his way, followed and beset by all the wrens in the vicinity. Slowly the scaly creature pushes himself up on the reeds; and as they bend under his weight he makes his way the more easily along them to the nest. His head is pushed in at the entrance, but an instant later the snake twines downward to the water. The nest was empty. Again he seeks an adjoining nest, and again is disappointed; and now, a small fish attracting his attention, he goes off in swift pursuit, leaving untouched the third nest in sight, that containing the precious eggs. Thus the apparently useless industry of the tiny wrens has served an invaluable end, and the tremulous chorus is again timidly taken up—little hymns of thanksgiving we may imagine them now.

These and many others are sights which a half-hour's tramp, without even wetting our shoes, may show us. Before we leave, hints of more deeply hidden secrets of the marsh may perhaps come to us. A swamp sparrow may show by its actions that its nest is not far away; from the depths of a ditch jungle the clatter of some rail comes faintly to our ears, and the distant croak of a night heron reaches us from its feeding-grounds, guarded by the deeper waters.

And what if behind me to westward the wall of the woods
    stands high?
The world lies east: how ample, the marsh and the sea and the
    sky!
A league and a league of marsh-grass, waist-high, broad in the
    blade.

Oh, what is abroad in the marsh and terminal sea?
Somehow my soul seems suddenly free
From the weighing of fate and the sad discussion of sin.

                        SIDNEY LANIER.

SECRETS OF THE OCEAN

WE are often held spellbound by the majesty of mountains, and indeed a lofty peak forever capped with snow, or pouring forth smoke and ashes, is impressive beyond all terrestrial things. But the ocean yields to nothing in its grandeur, in its age, in its ceaseless movement, and the question remains forever unanswered, "Who shall sound the mysteries of the sea?" Before the most ancient of mountains rose from the heart of the earth, the waves of the sea rolled as now, and though the edges of the continents shrink and expand, bend into bays or stretch out into capes, always through all the ages the sea follows and laps with ripples or booms with breakers unceasingly upon the shore.

Whether considered from the standpoint of the scientist, the mere curiosity of the tourist, or the keen delight of the enthusiastic lover of Nature, the shore of the sea—its sands and waters, its ever-changing skies and moods—is one of the most interesting spots in the world. The very bottom of the deep bays near shore—dark and eternally silent, prisoned under the restless waste of waters—is thickly carpeted with strange and many-coloured forms of animal and vegetable life. But the beaches and tide-pools over which the moon-urged tides hold sway in their ceaseless rise and fall, teem with marvels of Nature's handiwork, and every day are restocked and replanted with new living objects, both arctic and tropical offerings of each heaving tidal pulse.

Here on the northeastern shores of our continent one may spend days of leisure or delightful study among the abundant and ever changing variety of wonderful living creatures. It is not unlikely that the enjoyment and absolute novelty of this new world may enable one to look on these as some of the most pleasant days of life. I write from the edge of the restless waters of Fundy, but any rock-strewn shore will duplicate the marvels.

At high tide the surface of the Bay is unbroken by rock or shoal, and stretches glittering in the sunlight from the beach at one's feet to where the New Brunswick shore is just visible, appearing like a low bluish cloud on the horizon. At times the opposite shore is apparently brought nearer and made more distinct by a mirage, which inverts it, together with any ships which are in sight. A brig may be seen sailing along keel upward, in the most matter-of-fact way. The surface may anon be torn by those fearful squalls for which Fundy is noted, or, calm as a mirror, reflect the blue sky with an added greenish tinge, troubled only by the gentle alighting of a gull, the splash of a kingfisher or occasional osprey, as these dive for their prey, or the ruffling which shows where a school of mackerel is passing. This latter sign always sends the little sailing dories hurrying out, where they beat back and forth, like shuttles travelling across a loom, and at each turn a silvery struggling form is dragged into the boat.

A little distance along the shore the sandy beach ends and is replaced by huge bare boulders, scattered and piled in the utmost confusion. Back of these are scraggly spruces, with branches which have been so long blown landwards that they have bent and grown altogether on that side,—permanent weather-vanes of Fundy's storms. The very soil in which they began life was blown away, and their gnarled weather-worn roots hug the rocks, clutching every crevice as a drowning man would grasp an oar. On the side away from the bay two or three long, thick roots stretch far from each tree to the nearest earth-filled gully, sucking what scanty nourishment they can, for strength to withstand the winter's gales yet another year or decade. Beach-pea and sweet marsh lavender tint the sand, and stunted fringed orchids gleam in the coarse grass farther inland. High up among the rocks, where there is scarcely a handful of soil, delicate harebells sway and defy the blasts, enduring because of their very pliancy and weakness.

If we watch awhile we will see a line of blackish seaweed and wet sand appearing along the edge of the water, showing that the tide has turned and begun to recede. In an hour it has ebbed a considerable distance, and if we clamber down over the great weather-worn rocks the hardy advance guard of that wonderful world of life under the water is seen. Barnacles whiten the top of every rock which is reached by the tide, although the water may cover them only a short time each day. But they flourish here in myriads, and the shorter the chance they have at the salt water the more frantically their little feathery feet clutch at the tiny food particles which float around them. These thousands of tiny turreted castles are built so closely together that many are pressed out of shape, paralleling in shape as in substance the inorganic crystals of the mineral kingdom. The valved doors are continually opening and partly closing, and if we listen quietly we can hear a perpetual shuss! shuss! Is it the creaking of the tiny hinges? As the last receding wave splashes them, they shut their folding doors over a drop or two and remain tightly closed, while perhaps ten hours of sunlight bake them, or they glisten in the moonlight for the same length of time, ready at the first touch of the returning water to open wide and welcome it.

The thought of their life history brings to mind how sadly they retrogress as they grow, hatching as minute free-swimming creatures like tiny lobsters, and gradually changing to this plant-like life, *sans* eyes, *sans* head, *sans* most everything except a stomach and a few pairs of feathery feet to kick food into it. A few pitiful traces of nerves are left them. What if there were enough ganglia to enable them to dream of their past higher life, in the long intervals of patient waiting!

A little lower down we come to the zone of mussels,—hanging in clusters like some strange sea-fruit. Each is attached by strands of thin silky cables, so tough that they often defy our utmost efforts to tear a specimen away. How secure these creatures seem, how safe from all harm, and yet they have enemies which make havoc among them. At high tide fishes come and crunch them, shells and all, and multitudes of carnivorous snails are waiting to set their file-like tongues at work, which mercilessly drill through the lime shells, bringing death in a more subtle but no less certain form. Storms may tear away the support of these poor mollusks, and the waves dash them far out of the reach of the tides, while at low water, crows and gulls use all their ingenuity to get at their toothsome flesh.

There are no ant-hills in the sea, but when we turn over a large stone and see scores upon scores of small black shrimps scurrying around, the resemblance to those insects is striking. These little creatures quickly hitch away on their sides, getting out of sight in a remarkably short time.

The tide is going down rapidly, and following it step by step novel sights meet the eye at every turn, and we begin to realise that in this narrow strip, claimed alternately by sea and land, which would be represented on a map by the finest of hair-lines, there exists a complete world of animated life, comparing in variety and numbers with the life in that thinner medium, air. We climb over enormous boulders, so different in appearance that they would never be thought to consist of the same material as those higher up on the shore. These are masses of wave-worn rock, twenty or thirty feet across, piled in every imaginable position, and completely covered with a thick padding of seaweed. Their drapery of algæ hangs in festoons, and if we draw aside these submarine curtains, scenes from a veritable fairyland are disclosed. Deep pools of water, clear as crystal and icy cold, contain creatures both hideous and beautiful, sombre and iridescent, formless and of exquisite shape.

The sea-anemones first attract attention, showing as splashes of scarlet and salmon among the olive-green seaweed, or in hundreds covering the entire bottom of a pool with a delicately hued mist of waving tentacles. As the water leaves these exposed on the walls of the caves, they lose their plump appearance and, drawing in their wreath of tentacles, hang limp and shrivelled, resembling pieces of water-soaked meat as much as anything. Submerged in the icy water they are veritable animal-flowers. Their beauty is indeed well guarded, hidden by the overhanging seaweed in these caves twenty-five feet or more below high-water mark.

Here in these beautiful caverns we may make aquariums, and transplant as many animal-flowers as we wish. Wherever we place them their fleshy, snail-like foot spreads out, takes tight hold, and the creature lives content, patiently waiting for the Providence of the sea to send food to its many wide-spread fingers.

Carpeted with pink algæ and dainty sponges, draped with sea-lettuce like green tissue paper, decorated with strange corallines, these natural aquariums far surpass any of artificial make. Although the tide drives us from them sooner or later, we may return with the sure prospect of finding them refreshed and perhaps replenished with many new forms. For often some of the deep-water creatures are held prisoners in the lower tide-pools, as the water settles, somewhat as when the glaciers receded northward after the Ice Age there were left on isolated mountain peaks traces of the boreal fauna and flora.

If we are interested enough to watch our anemones we will find much entertainment. Let us return to our shrimp colonies and bring a handful to our pool. Drop one in the centre of an anemone and see how quickly it contracts. The tentacles bend over it exactly as the sticky hairs of the sun-dew plant close over a fly. The shrimp struggles for a moment and is then drawn downward out of sight. The birth of an anemone is well worth patient watching, and this may take place in several different ways. We may see a large individual with a number of tiny bunches on the sides of the body, and if we keep this one in a tumbler, before long these protuberances will be seen to develop a few tentacles and at last break off as perfect miniature anemones. Or again, an anemone may draw in its tentacles without apparent cause, and after a few minutes expand more widely than ever. Suddenly a movement of the mouth is seen, and it opens, and one, two, or even a half-dozen tiny anemones shoot forth. They turn and roll in the little spurt of water and gradually settle to the rock alongside of the mother. In a short time they turn right side up, expand their absurd little heads, and begin life for themselves. These animal "buds" may be of all sizes; some minute ones will be much less developed and look very unlike the parent. These are able to swim about for a while, and myriads of them may be born in an hour. Others, as we have seen, have tentacles and settle down at once.

Fishes, little and big, are abundant in the pools, darting here and there among the leathery fronds of "devils' aprons," cavernous-mouthed angler fish, roly-poly young lump-suckers, lithe butter-fish, and many others.

Moving slowly through the pools are many

beautiful creatures, some so evanescent that they
are only discoverable by the faint shadows which
they cast on the bottom, others suggest animated
spheres of prismatic sunlight. These latter are
tiny jelly-fish, circular hyaline masses of jelly with
eight longitudinal bands, composed of many
comb-like plates, along which iridescent waves of
light continually play. The graceful appearance
of these exquisite creatures is increased by two
long, fringed tentacles streaming behind, drifting
at full length or contracting into numerous coils.
The fringe on these streamers is a series of living
hairs—an aquatic cobweb, each active with life,
and doing its share in ensnaring minute atoms of
food for its owner. When dozens of these
ctenophores (or comb-bearers)' as they are called,
glide slowly to and fro through a pool, the sight is
not soon forgotten. To try to photograph them
is like attempting to portray the substance of a
sunbeam, but patience works wonders, and even a
slightly magnified image of a living jelly is
secured, which shows very distinctly all the details of its wonderfully simple structure; the
pouch, suspended in the centre of the sphere,
which does duty as a stomach; the sheaths into
which the long tentacles may be so magically
packed, and the tiny organ at the top of this living
ball of spun glass, serving, with its minute weights
and springs, as compass, rudder, and pilot to this
little creature, which does not fear to pit its

muscles of jelly against the rush and might of breaking waves.

Even the individual comb-plates or rows of oars are plainly seen, although, owing to their rapid motion, they appear to the naked eye as a single band of scintillating light. This and other magnified photographs were obtained by fastening the lens of a discarded bicycle lantern in a cone of paper blackened on the inside with shoe-blacking. With this crude apparatus placed in front of the lens of the camera, the evanescent beauties of these most delicate creatures were preserved.

Other equally beautiful forms of jelly-fish are balloon-shaped. These are *Beröe,* fitly named after the daughter of the old god Oceanus. They, like others of their family, pulsate through the water, sweeping gracefully along, borne on currents of their own making.

Passing to other inhabitants of the pools, we find starfish and sea-urchins everywhere abundant. Hunched-up groups of the former show where they are dining in their unique way on unfortunate sea-snails or anemones, protruding their whole stomach and thus engulfing their victim. The urchins strain and stretch with their innumerable sucker-feet, feeling for something to grasp, and in this laborious way pull themselves along. The mouth, with the five so-called teeth, is a conspicuous feature, visible at the centre of the urchin and surrounded by the greenish spines.

Some of the starfish are covered with long spines, others are nearly smooth. The colours are wonderfully varied,—red, purple, orange, yellow, etc.

The stages through which these prickly skinned animals pass, before they reach the adult state, are wonderfully curious, and only when they are seen under the microscope can they be fully appreciated. A bolting-cloth net drawn through some of the pools will yield thousands in many stages, and we can take eggs of the common starfish and watch their growth in tumblers of water. At first the egg seems nothing but a tiny round globule of jelly, but soon a dent or depression appears on one side, which becomes deeper and deeper until it extends to the centre of the egg-mass. It is as if we should take a round ball of putty and gradually press our finger into it. This pressed-in sac is a kind of primitive stomach and the entrance is used as a mouth. After this follows a marvellous succession of changes, form giving place to form, differing more in appearance and structure from the five-armed starfish than a caterpillar differs from a butterfly.

For example, when about eight days old, another mouth has formed and two series of delicate cilia or swimming hairs wind around the creature, by means of which it glides slowly through the water. The photographs of a starfish of this age show the stomach with its contents, a dark rounded mass near the lower portion of the

organism. The vibrating bands which outline the
tiny animal are also visible. The delicacy of structure and difficulty of preserving these young starfish alive make these pictures of particular value,
especially as they were taken of the living forms
swimming in their natural element. Each day
and almost each hour adds to the complexity of
the little animal, lung tentacles grow out and
many other larval stages are passed through
before the starfish shape is discernible within this
curious "nurse" or living, changing egg. Then
the entire mass, so elaborately evolved through
so long a time, is absorbed and the little baby star
sinks to the bottom to start on its new life, crawling around and over whatever happens in its path
and feeding to repletion on succulent oysters. It
can laugh at the rage of the oysterman, who
angrily tears it in pieces, for "time heals all
wounds" literally in the case of these creatures,
and even if the five arms are torn apart, five starfish, small of arm but with healthy stomachs, will
soon be foraging on the oyster bed.

But to return to our tide-pools. In the skim-
ming net with the young starfish many other creatures are found, some so delicate and fragile that
they disintegrate before microscope and camera
can be placed in position. I lie at full length on
a soft couch of seaweed with my face close to a
tiny pool no larger than my hand. A few arma-
dillo shells and limpets crawl on the bottom, but

a frequent troubling of the water baffles me. I
make sure my breath has nothing to do with it,
but still it continues. At last a beam of sunshine
lights up the pool, and as if a film had rolled from
my eyes I see the cause of the disturbance. A sea-
worm—or a ghost of one—is swimming about. Its
large, brilliant eyes, long tentacles, and innumerable waving appendages are now as distinct as
before they had been invisible. A trifling change
in my position and all vanishes as if by magic.
There seems not an organ, not a single part of
the creature, which is not as transparent as the
water itself. The fine streamers into which the
paddles and gills are divided are too delicate to
have existence in any but a water creature, and
the least attempt to lift the animal from its element would only tear and dismember it, so I leave
it in the pool to await the return of the tide.

Shrimps and prawns of many shapes and colours inhabit every pool. One small species,
abundant on the algæ, combines the colour changes
of a chameleon with the form and manner of
travel of a measuring-worm, looping along the
fronds of seaweed or swimming with the same
motion. Another variety of shrimp resembles
the common wood-louse found under pieces of
bark, but is most beautifully iridescent, glowing
like an opal at the bottom of the pool. The curious little sea-spiders keep me guessing for a long
time where their internal organs can be, as they

consist of legs with merely enough body to connect these firmly together. The fact that the thread-like stomach and other organs send a branch into each of the eight legs explains the mystery and shows how far economy of space may go. Their skeleton-forms, having the appearance of eight straggling filaments of seaweed, are thus, doubtless, a great protection to these creatures from their many enemies. Other hobgoblin forms with huge probosces crawl slowly over the floors of the anemone caves, or crouch as the shadow of my hand or net falls upon them.

The larger gorgeously coloured and graceful sea-worms contribute not a small share to the beauty of Fundy tide-pools, swimming in iridescent waves through the water or waving their Medusa-head of crimson tentacles at the bottom among the sea-lettuce. These worms form tubes of mud for themselves, and the rows of hooks on each side of the body enable them to climb up and down in their dismal homes.

Much of the seaweed from deeper bottoms seems to be covered with a dense fur, which under a hand lens resolves into beautiful hydroids,— near relatives of the anemones and corals. Scientists have happily given these most euphonious names—*Campanularia*, *Obelia*, and *Plumularia*. Among the branches of certain of these, numbers of round discs or spheres are visible. These are young medusæ or jelly-fish, which grow

like bunches of currants, and later will break off
and swim around at pleasure in the water. Occasionally one is fortunate enough to discover these
small jellies in a pool where they can be photographed as they pulsate back and forth. When
these attain their full size they lay eggs which
sink to the bottom and grow up into the plant-like
hydroids. So each generation of these interesting
creatures is entirely unlike that which immediately precedes or follows it. In other words, a
hydroid is exactly like its grandmother and grand-
daughter, but as different from its parents and
children in appearance as a plant is from an animal. Even in a fairy-story book this would be
wonderful, but here it is taking place under our
very eyes, as are scores of other transformations
and "miracles in miniature" in this marvellous
underworld.

Now let us deliberately pass by all the attrac-
tions of the middle zone of tide-pools and on as
far as the lowest level of the water will admit.
We are far out from the shore and many feet
below the level of the barnacle-covered boulders
over which we first clambered. Now we may
indeed be prepared for strange sights, for we are
on the very border-land of the vast unknown. The
abyss in front of us is like planetary space, unknown to the feet of man. While we know the latter by scant glimpses through our telescopes, the
former has only been scratched by the hauls of

the dredge, the mark of whose iron shoe is like the tiny track of a snail on the leaf mould of a vast forest.

The first plunge beneath the icy waters of Fundy is likely to remain long in one's memory, and one's first dive of short duration, but the glimpse which is had and the hastily snatched handfuls of specimens of the beauties which no tide ever uncovers is potent to make one forget his shivering and again and again seek to penetrate as far as a good-sized stone and a lungful of air will carry him. Strange sensations are experienced in these aquatic scrambles. It takes a long time to get used to pulling oneself *downward,* or propping your knees against the *under* crevices of rocks. To all intents and purposes, the law of gravitation is partly suspended, and when stone and wooden wedge accidentally slip from one's hand and disappear in *opposite* directions, it is confusing, to say the least.

When working in one spot for some time the fishes seem to become used to one, and approach quite closely. Slick-looking pollock, bloated lump-fish, and occasionally a sombre dog-fish rolls by, giving one a start, as the memory of pictures of battles between divers and sharks of tropical waters comes to mind. One's mental impressions made thus are somewhat disconnected. With the blood buzzing in the ears, it is only possible to snatch general glimpses and superficial details.

Then at the surface, notes can be made, and specimens which have been overlooked, felt for during the next trip beneath the surface. Fronds of laminaria yards in length, like sheets of rubber, offer convenient holds, and at their roots many curious creatures make their home. Serpent starfish, agile as insects and very brittle, are abundant, and new forms of worms, like great slugs,—their backs covered with gills in the form of tufted branches.

In these outer, eternally submerged regions are starfish of still other shapes, some with a dozen or more arms. I took one with thirteen rays and placed it temporarily in a pool aquarium with some large anemones. On returning in an hour or two I found the starfish trying to make a meal of the largest anemone. Hundreds of dart-covered strings had been pushed out by the latter in defence, but they seemed to cause the starfish no inconvenience whatever.

In my submarine glimpses I saw spaces free from seaweed on which hundreds of tall polyps were growing, some singly, others in small tufts. The solitary individuals rise three or four inches by a nearly straight stalk, surmounted by a many-tentacled head. This droops gracefully to one side and the general effect is that of a bed of rose-coloured flowers. From the heads hang grape-like masses, which on examination in a tumbler are seen to be immature medusæ. Each of these develop to the point where the four radiating canals are discernible and then their growth comes to a standstill, and they never attain the freedom for which their structure fits them.

When the wind blew inshore, I would often find the water fairly alive with large sun-jellies or *Aurelia,*—their Latin name. Their great milky-white bodies would come heaving along and bump against me, giving a very "crawly" sensation. The circle of short tentacles and the four horse-shoe-shaped ovaries distinguish this jelly-fish from all others. When I had gone down as far as I dared, I would sometimes catch glimpses of these strange beings far below me, passing and repassing in the silence and icy coldness of the watery depths. These large medusæ are often very abundant after a favourable wind has blown for a few days, and I have rowed through masses of them so thick that it seemed like rowing through thick jelly, two or three feet deep. In an area the length of the boat and about a yard wide, I have counted over one hundred and fifty *Aurelias* on the surface alone.

When one of these "sun-fish," as the fishermen call them, is lifted from the water, the clay-coloured eggs may be seen to stream from it in myriads. In many jellies, small bodies the size of a pea are visible in the interior of the mass, and when extracted they prove to be a species of small shrimp. These are well adapted for their quasi-parasitic life, in colour being throughout of the same milky semi-opaqueness as their host, but one very curious thing about them is, that when taken out and placed in some water in a vial or tumbler they begin to turn darker almost immediately, and in five minutes all will be of various shades, from red to a dark brown.

I had no fear of *Aurelia,* but when another free-swimming species of jelly-fish, *Cyanea,* or the blue-jelly, appeared, I swam ashore with all speed. This great jelly is usually more of a reddish liver-colour than a purple, and is much to be dreaded. Its tentacles are of enormous length. I have seen specimens which measured two feet across the disc, with streamers fully forty feet long, and one has been recorded seven feet across and no less than one hundred and twelve feet to the tip of the cruel tentacles! These trail behind in eight bunches and form a living, tangled labyrinth as deadly as the hair of the fabled Medusa—whose name indeed has been so appropriately applied to this division of animals. The touch of each tentacle to the skin is like a lash of nettle, and there would be little hope for a diver whose path crossed such a fiery tangle. The untold myriads of little darts which are shot out secrete a poison which is terribly irritating.

On the crevice bottoms a sight now and then meets my eyes which brings the "devil-fish" of Victor Hugo's romance vividly to mind,—a misshapen squid making its way snakily over the shells and seaweed. Its large eyes gaze fixedly around and the arms reach alternately forward, the sucking cups lined with their cruel teeth closing over the inequalities of the bottom. The creature may suddenly change its mode of progression and shoot like an arrow, backward and upward. If we watch one in its passage over areas of seaweed and sand, a wonderful adaptation becomes apparent. Its colour changes continually; when near sand it is of a sombre brown hue, then blushes of colour pass over it and the tint changes, corresponding to the seaweed or patches of pink sponge over which it swims. The way in which this is accomplished is very ingenious and loses nothing by examination. Beneath the skin are numerous cells filled with liquid pigment. When at rest these contract until they are almost invisible, appearing as very small specks or dots on the surface of the body. When the animal wishes to change its hue, certain muscles which radiate from these colour cells are shortened, drawing the cells out in all directions until they seem confluent. It is as if the freckles on a person's face should be all joined together, when an ordinary tan would result.

From bottoms ten to twenty fathoms below the surface, deeper than mortal eye can probably ever hope to reach, the dredge brings up all manner of curious things; basket starfish, with arms divided and subdivided into many tendrils, on the tips of which it walks, the remaining part converging upward like the trellis of a vine-covered summer house. Sponges of many hues must fairly carpet large areas of the deep water, as the dredge is often loaded with them. The small shore-loving ones which I photographed are in perfect health, but the camera cannot show the many tiny currents of water pouring in food and oxygen at the smaller openings, and returning in larger streams from the tall funnels on the surface of the sponge, which a pinch of carmine dust reveals so beautifully. From the deeper aquatic gardens come up great orange and yellow sponges, two and three feet in length, and around the bases of these the weird serpent stars are clinging, while crabs scurry away as the mass reaches the surface of the water.

Treasures from depths of forty and even fifty fathoms can be obtained when a trip is taken with the trawl-men. One can sit fascinated for hours, watching the hundreds of yards of line reel in, with some interesting creature on each of the thirty-seven hundred odd hooks. At times a glance down into the clear water will show a score of fish in sight at once, hake, haddock, cod, halibut, dog-fish, and perhaps an immense "barndoor" skate, a yard or more square. This latter will hold back with frantic flaps of its great "wings," and tax all the strength of the sturdy Acadian fishermen to pull it to the gunwale.

Now and then a huge "meat-rock," the fishermen's apt name for an anemone, comes up, impaled on a hook, and still clinging to a stone of five to ten pounds weight. These gigantic scarlet ones from full fifty fathoms far surpass any near shore. Occasionally the head alone of a large fish will appear, with the entire body bitten clean off, a hint of the monsters which must haunt the lower depths. The pressure of the air must be excessive, for many of the fishes have their swimming bladders fairly forced out of their mouths by the lessening of atmospheric pressure as they are drawn to the surface. When a basket starfish finds one of the baits in that sunless void far beneath our boat, he hugs it so tenaciously that the upward jerks of the reel only make him hold the more tightly.

Once in a great while the fishermen find what they call a "knob-fish" on one of their hooks, and I never knew what they meant until one day a small colony of five was brought ashore. *Boltenia,* the scientists call them, tall, queer-shaped things; a stalk six to eight inches in length, with a knob or oblong bulb-like body at the summit, looking exactly like the flower of a lady-slipper orchid and as delicately coloured. This is a member of that curious family of Ascidians, which forever trembles in the balance between the higher back-boned animals and the lower division, where are classified the humbler insects, crabs, and snails. The young of *Boltenia* promises everything in its tiny backbone or notochord, but it all ends in promise, for that shadow of a great ambition withers away, and the creature is doomed to a lowly and vegetative life. If we soften the hard scientific facts which tell us of these dumb, blind creatures, with the humane mellowing thought of the oneness of all life, we will find much that is pathetic and affecting in their humble biographies from our point of view. And yet these cases of degeneration are far from anything like actual misfortunes, or mishaps of nature, as Buffon was so fond of thinking. These creatures have found their adult mode of life more free from competition than any other, and hence their adoption of it. It is only another instance of exquisite adaptation to an unfilled niche in the life of the world.

Yet another phase of enjoying the life of these northern waters; the one which comes after all the work and play of collecting is over for the day, after the last specimen is given a fresh supply of water for the night, and the final note in our journal is written. Then, as dusk falls, we make our way to the beach, ship our rudder and oars and push slowly along shore, or drift quietly with the tide. The stars may come out in clear splendour and the visual symphony of the northern lights play over the dark vault above us, or all may be obscured in lowering, leaden clouds. But the lights of the sea are never obscured—they always shine with a splendour which keeps one entranced for hours.

At night the ripples and foam of the Fundy shores seem transformed to molten silver and gold, and after each receding wave the emerald seaweed is left dripping with millions of sparkling lights, shining with a living lustre which would pale the brightest gem. Each of these countless sparks is a tiny animal, as perfect in its substance and as well adapted to its cycle of life as the highest created being. The wonderful way in which this phosphorescence permeates everything—the jelly-fish seeming elfish fireworks as they throb through the water with rhythmic beats —the fish brilliantly lighted up and plainly visible as they dart about far beneath the surface—makes such a night on the Bay of Fundy an experience to be always remembered.

> Like the tints on a crescent sea beach
>   When the moon is new and thin,
> Into our hearts high yearnings
>   Come welling and surging in—
> Come, from the mystic ocean,
>   Whose rim no foot has trod—
> Some of us call it longing,
>   And others call it God.
>   W. H. CARRUTH.

JULY.

BIRDS IN A CITY

W E frequently hear people say that if only they lived in the country they would take up the study of birds with great interest, but that a city life prevented any nature study. To show how untrue this is, I once made a census of wild birds which were nesting in the New York Zoological Park, which is situated within the limits of New York City. Part of the Park is wooded, while much space is given up to the collections of birds and animals. Throughout the year thousands of people crowd the walks and penetrate to every portion of the grounds; yet in spite of this lack of seclusion no fewer than sixty-one species build their nests here and successfully rear their young. The list was made without shooting a single bird and in each instance the identification was absolute. This shows what a little protection will accomplish, while many places of equal area in the country which are harried by boys and cats are tenanted by a bare dozen species.

Let us see what a walk in late June, or especially in July, will show of these bold invaders of our very city. Wild wood ducks frequently decoy to the flocks of pinioned birds and sometimes mate with some of them. One year a wild bird chose as its mate a little brown female, a pinioned bird, and refused to desert her even when the brood of summer ducklings was being caught and pinioned. Such devotion is rare indeed.

In the top of one of the most inaccessible trees in the Park a great rough nest of sticks shows where a pair of black-crowned night herons have made their home for years, and from the pale green eggs hatch the most awkward of nestling herons, which squawk and grow to their prime, on a diet of small fish. When they are able to fly they pay frequent visits to their relations in the great flying cage, perching on the top and gazing with longing eyes at the abundant feasts of fish which are daily brought by the keepers to their charges. This duck and heron are the only ones of their orders thus to honour the Park by nesting, although a number of other species are not uncommon during the season of migration.

Of the waders which in the spring and fall teeter along the bank of the Bronx River, only a pair or two of spotted sandpipers remain throughout the nesting period, content to lay their eggs in some retired spot in the corner of a field, where there is the least danger to them and to the fluffy balls of long-legged down which later appear and scurry about. The great horned owl and the red-tailed hawk formerly nested in the park, but the frequent noise of blasting and the building operations have driven them to more isolated places, and of their relatives there remain only the little screech owls and the sparrow hawks. The latter feed chiefly upon English sparrows and hence are worthy of the most careful protection.

These birds should be encouraged to build near our homes, and if not killed or driven away sometimes choose the eaves of our houses as their domiciles and thus, by invading the very haunts of the sparrows, they would speedily lessen their numbers. A brood of five young hawks was recently taken from a nest under the eaves of a schoolhouse in this city. I immediately took this as a text addressed to the pupils, and the principal was surprised to learn that these birds were so valuable. In the Park the sparrow hawks nest in a hollow tree, as do the screech owls.

Other most valuable birds which nest in the Park are the black-billed and yellow-billed cuckoos, whose depredations among the hairy and spiny caterpillars should arouse our gratitude. For these insects are refused by almost all other birds, and were it not for these slim, graceful creatures they would increase to prodigious numbers. Their two or three light blue eggs are always laid on the frailest of frail platforms made of a few sticks. The belted kingfisher bores into the bank of the river and rears his family of six or eight in the dark, ill-odoured chamber at the end. Young cuckoos and kingfishers are the quaintest of young birds. Their plumage does not come out a little

at a time, as in other nestlings, but the sheaths
which surround the growing feathers remain until
they are an inch or more in length; then one day,
in the space of only an hour or so, the overlapping
armour of bluish tiles bursts and the plumage
assumes a normal appearance.

The little black-and-white downy and the flicker
are the two woodpeckers which make the Park
their home. Both nest in hollows bored out by
their strong beaks, but although full of splinters
and sawdust, such a habitation is far superior to
the sooty chimneys in which the young chimney
swifts break from their snow-white eggs and
twitter for food. How impatiently they must look
up at the blue sky, and one would think that they
must long for the time when they can spread their
sickle-shaped wings and dash about from dawn
to dark! Is it not wonderful that one of them
should live to grow up when we think of the fragile little cup which is their home?—a mosaic of
delicate twigs held together only by the sticky
saliva of the parent birds.

A relation of theirs—though we should never
guess it—is sitting upon her tiny air castle high
up in an apple tree not far away,—a ruby-throated
hummingbird. If we take a peep into the nest
when the young hummingbirds are only partly
grown, we shall see that their bills are broad and
stubby, like those of the swifts. Their home, however, is indeed a different affair,—a pinch of

plant-down tied together with cobwebs and stuccoed with lichens, like those which are growing all about upon the tree. If we do not watch the female when she settles to her young or eggs we may search in vain for this tiniest of homes, so closely does it resemble an ordinary knot on a branch.

The flycatchers are well represented in the Park, there being no fewer than five species; the least flycatcher, wood pewee, phœbe, crested flycatcher, and kingbird. The first two prefer the woods, the phœbe generally selects a mossy rock or a bridge beam, the fourth nests in a hollow tree and often decorates its home with a snake-skin. The kingbird builds an untidy nest in an apple tree. Our American crow is, of course, a member of this little community of birds, and that in spite of persecution, for in the spring one or two are apt to contract a taste for young ducklings and hence have to be put out of the way. The fish crow, a smaller cousin of the big black fellow, also nests here, easily known by his shriller, higher caw. A single pair of blue jays nest in the Park, but the English starling occupies every box which is put up and bids fair to be as great or a greater nuisance than the sparrow. It is a handsome bird and a fine whistler, but when we remember how this foreigner is slowly but surely elbowing our native birds out of their rightful haunts, we find ourselves losing sight of its beauties. The cowbird, of course, imposes her eggs upon many of the smaller species of birds, while our beautiful purple grackle, meadow lark, red-winged blackbird, and the Baltimore and orchard orioles rear their young in safety. The cardinal, scarlet tanager, indigo bunting, and rose-breasted grosbeak form a quartet of which even a tropical land might well be proud, and the two latter species have, in addition to brilliant plumage, very pleasing songs. Such wealth of æsthetic characteristics are unusual in any one species, the wide-spread law of compensation decreeing otherwise. More sombre hued seed-eaters which live their lives in the Park are towhees, swamp, song, field, and chipping sparrows. The bank and barn swallows skim over field and pond all through the summer, gleaning their insect harvest from the air, and building their nests in the places from which they have taken their names. The rare rough-winged swallow deigns to linger and nest in the Park as well as do his more common brethren.

The dainty pensile nests which become visible when the leaves fall in the autumn are swung by four species of vireos, the white-eyed, red-eyed, warbling, and yellow-throated. Of the interesting and typically North American family of wood warblers I have numbered no fewer than eight which nest in the Park; these are the redstart, the yellow-breasted chat, northern yellow-throat, oven-bird, the yellow warbler, blue-winged, black-

and-white creeping warblers, and one other to be
mentioned later.

Injurious insects find their doom when the
young house and Carolina wrens are on the wing.
Catbirds and robins are among the most abundant
breeders, while chickadees and white-breasted
nuthatches are less often seen. The bluebird
haunts the hollow apple trees, and of the thrushes
proper the veery or Wilson's and the splendid
wood thrush sing to their mates on the nests
among the saplings.

The rarest of all the birds which I have found
nesting in the Park is a little yellow and green
warbler, with a black throat and sides of the face,
known as the Lawrence warbler. Only a few of
his kind have ever been seen, and strange to say
his mate was none other than a demure blue-
winged warbler. His nest was on the ground and
from it six young birds flew to safety and not to
museum drawers.

NIGHT MUSIC OF THE SWAMP

TO many, a swamp or marsh brings only the very practical thought of whether it can be readily drained. Let us rejoice, however, that many marshes cannot be thus easily wiped out of existence, and hence they remain as isolated bits of primeval wilderness, hedged about by farms and furrows. The water is the life-blood of the marsh,—drain it, and reed and rush, bird and batrachian, perish or disappear. The marsh, to him who enters it in a receptive mood, holds, besides mosquitoes and stagnation,—melody, the mystery of unknown waters, and the sweetness of Nature undisturbed·by man.

The ideal marsh is as far as one can go from civilisation. The depths of a wood holds its undiscovered secrets; the mysterious call of the veery lends a wildness that even to-day has not ceased to pervade the old wood. There are spots overgrown with fern and carpeted with velvety wet moss; here also the skunk cabbage and cowslip grow rank among the alders. Surely man cannot live near this place—but the tinkle of a cowbell comes faintly on the gentle stirring breeze—and our illusion is dispelled, the charm is broken.

But even to-day, when we push the punt through the reeds from the clear river into the narrow, tortuous channel of the marsh, we have left civilisation behind us. The great ranks of the cattails shut out all view of the outside world; the distant sounds of civilisation serve only to accentuate the isolation. It is the land of the Indian, as it was before the strange white man, brought from afar in great white-sailed ships, came to usurp the land of the wondering natives. At any moment we fancy that we may see an Indian canoe silently round a bend in the channel.

The marsh has remained unchanged since the days when the Mohican Indians speared fish there. We are living in a bygone time. A little green heron flies across the water. How wild he is; nothing has tamed him. He also is the same now as always. He does not nest in orchard or meadow, but holds himself aloof, making no concessions to man and the ever increasing spread of his civilisation. He does not come to his doors for food. He can find food for himself and in abundance; he asks only to be let alone. Nor does he intrude himself. Occasionally we meet him along our little meadow stream, but he makes no advances. As we come suddenly upon him, how indignant he seems at being disturbed in his hunting. Like the Indian, he is jealous of his ancient domain and resents intrusion. He retires, however, throwing back to us a cry of disdain. Here in the marsh is the last stand of primitive nature in the settled country; here is the last stronghold of the untamed. The bulrushes rise in ranks, like the spears of a great army, surrounding and guarding the colony of the marsh.

There seems to be a kinship between the voices of the marsh dwellers. Most of them seem to have a muddy, aquatic note. The boom of the frog sounds like some great stone dropped into the water; the little marsh wren's song is the "babble and tinkle of water running out of a silver flask."

The blackbird seems to be the one connecting link between the highlands and the lowlands. Seldom does one see other citizens of the marsh in the upland. How glorious is the flight of a great blue heron from one feeding-ground to another! He does not tarry over the foreign territory, nor does he hurry. With neck and head furled close and legs straight out behind, he pursues his course, swerving neither to the right nor the left.

> "Vainly the fowler's eye
> Might mark thy distant flight to do thee wrong,
> As darkly painted on the crimson sky
> Thy figure floats along."

The blackbirds, however, are more neighbourly. They even forage in the foreign territory, returning at night to sleep.

In nesting time the red-wing is indeed a citizen of the lowland. His voice is as distinctive of the marsh as is the croak of the frog, and from a distance it is one of the first sounds to greet the ear. How beautiful is his clear whistle with its liquid break! Indeed one may say that he is the most conspicuous singer of the marshlands. His is not a sustained song, but the exuberant expression of a happy heart.

According to many writers the little marsh wren is without song. No song! As well say that the farmer boy's whistling as he follows the plough, or the sailor's song as he hoists the sail, is not music! All are the songs of the lowly, the melody of those glad to be alive and out in the free air.

When man goes into the marsh, the marsh retires within itself, as a turtle retreats within his shell. With the exception of a few blackbirds and marsh wrens, babbling away the nest secret, and an occasional frog's croak, all the inhabitants have stealthily retired. The spotted turtle has slid from the decayed log as the boat pushed through the reeds. At our approach the heron has flown and the little Virginia rail has scuttled away among the reeds.

Remain perfectly quiet, however, and give the marsh time to regain its composure. One by one the tenants of the swamp will take up the trend of their business where it was interrupted.

All about, the frogs rest on the green carpet of the lily pads, basking in the sun. The little rail again runs among the reeds, searching for food in the form of small snails. The blackbirds and

wrens, most domestic in character, go busily about
their home business; the turtles again come up to
their positions, and a muskrat swims across the
channel. One hopes that the little colony of marsh
wren homes on stilts above the water, like the
ancient lake dwellers of Tenochtitlan, may have
no enemies. But the habit of building dummy
nests is suggestive that the wee birds are pitting
their wits against the cunning of some enemy,—
and suspicion rests upon the serpent.

As evening approaches and the shadows from
the bordering wood point long fingers across the
marsh, the blackbirds straggle back from their
feeding-grounds and settle, clattering, among the
reeds. Their clamour dies gradually away and
night settles down upon the marsh.

.   .   .   .

All sounds have ceased save the booming of the
frogs, which but emphasises the loneliness of it
all. A distant whistle of a locomotive dispels the
idea that all the world is wilderness. The firefly
lamps glow along the margin of the rushes. The
frogs are now in full chorus, the great bulls beating their tom-toms and the small fry filling in the
chinks with shriller cries. How remote the scene
and how melancholy the chorus!

To one mind there is a quality in the frogs'
serenade that strikes the chord of sadness, to

another the chord of contentment, to still another it is the chant of the savage, just as the hoot of an owl or the bark of a fox brings vividly to mind the wilderness.

Out of the night comes softly the croon of a little screech owl—that cry almost as ancient as the hills. It belongs with the soil beneath our towns. It is the spirit of the past crying to us. So the dirge of the frog is the cry of the spirit of river and marshland.

Our robins and bluebirds are of the orchard and the home of man, but who can claim neighbourship to the bittern or the bullfrog? There is nothing of civilisation in the hoarse croak of the great blue heron. These are all barbarians and their songs are of the untamed wilderness.

The moon rises over the hills. The mosquitoes have become savage. The marsh has tolerated us as long as it cares to, and we beat our retreat. The night hawks swoop down and boom as they pass overhead. One feels thankful that the mosquitoes are of some good in furnishing food to so graceful a bird.

A water snake glides across the channel, leaving a silver wake in the moonlight. The frogs plunk into the water as we push past. A night heron rises from the margin of the river and slowly flops away. The bittern booms again as we row down the peaceful river, and we leave the marshland to its ancient and rightful owners.

And the marsh is meshed with a million veins,
That like as with rosy and silvery essences flow
In the rose and silver evening glow.
   Farewell, my lord Sun!
The creeks overflow; a thousand rivulets run
'Twixt the roots of the sod; the blades of the marsh grass stir;
Passeth a hurrying sound of wings that westward whirr.
         SIDNEY LANIER.

THE COMING OF MAN

IF we betake ourselves to the heart of the deepest forests which are still left upon our northern hills, and compare the bird life which we find there with that in the woods and fields near our homes, we shall at once notice a great difference. Although the coming of mankind with his axe and plough has driven many birds and animals far away or actually exterminated them, there are many others which have so thrived under the new conditions that they are far more numerous than when the tepees of the red men alone broke the monotony of the forest.

We might walk all day in the primitive woods and never see or hear a robin, while in an hour's stroll about a village we can count scores. Let us observe how some of these quick-witted feathered beings have taken advantage of the way in which man is altering the whole face of the land.

A pioneer comes to a spot in the virgin forest which pleases him and proceeds at once to cut down the trees in order to make a clearing. The hermit thrush soothes his labour with its wonderful song; the pileated woodpecker pounds its disapproval upon a near-by hollow tree; the deer and wolf take a last look out through the trees and flee from the spot forever. A house and barn arise; fields become covered with waving grass and grain; a neglected patch of burnt forest becomes a tangle of blackberry and raspberry; an orchard is set out.

When the migrating birds return, they are attracted to this new scene. The decaying wood of fallen trees is a paradise for ants, flies, and beetles; offering to swallows, creepers, and flycatchers feasts of abundance never dreamed of in the primitive forests. Straightway, what must have been a cave swallow becomes a barn swallow; the haunter of rock ledges changes to an eave swallow; the nest in the niche of the cliff is deserted and phœbe becomes a bridgebird; cedarbirds are renamed cherrybirds, and catbirds and other low-nesting species find the blackberry patch safer than the sweetbrier vine in the deep woods. The swift leaves the lightning-struck hollow tree where owl may harry or snake intrude, for the chimney flue—sooty but impregnable.

When the great herds of ruminants disappear from the western prairies, the buffalo birds without hesitation become cowbirds, and when the plough turns up the never-ending store of grubs and worms the birds lose all fear and follow at the very heels of the plough-boy: grackles, vesper sparrows, and larks in the east, and flocks of gulls farther to the westward.

The crow surpasses all in the keen wit which it pits against human invasion and enmity. The

farmer declares war (all unjustly) against these
sable natives, but they jeer at his gun and traps
and scarecrows, and thrive on, killing the noxious
insects, devouring the diseased corn-sprouts,—
doing great good to the farmer in spite of himself.

The story of these sudden adaptations to conditions which the birds could never have foreseen
is a story of great interest and it has been but half
told.   Climb the nearest hill or mountain or even a
tall tree and look out upon the face of the country.
Keep in mind you are a bird and not a human,—
you neither know nor understand anything of
the reason for these strange sights,—these bipeds
who cover the earth with great square structures,
who scratch the ground for miles, who later gnaw
the vegetation with great shining teeth, and who
are only too often on the look out to bring sudden
death if one but show a feather.   What would you
do?

THE SILENT LANGUAGE OF ANIMALS

WHAT a great difference there is in brilliancy of colouring between birds and the furry creatures. How the plumage of a cardinal, or indigo bunting, or hummingbird glows in the sunlight, and reflects to our eyes the most intense vermilion or indigo or an iridescence of the whole gamut of colour. On the other hand, how somberly clad are the deer, the rabbits, and the mice; gray and brown and white being the usual hue of their fur.

This difference is by no means accidental, but has for its cause a deep significance,—all-important to the life of the bird or mammal. Scientists have long known of it, and if we unlock it from its hard sheathing of technical terms, we shall find it as simple and as easy to understand as it is interesting. When we once hold the key, it will seem as if scales had fallen from our eyes, and when we take our walks abroad through the fields and woods, when we visit a zoological park, or even see the animals in a circus, we shall feel as though a new world were opened to us.

No post offices, or even addresses, exist for birds and mammals; when the children of the desert or the jungle are lost, no detective or policeman hastens to find them, no telephone or telegraph aids in the search. Yet, without any of these accessories, the wild creatures have marvellous systems of communication. The five senses (and perhaps a mysterious sixth, at which we can only guess) are the telephones and the police, the automatic sentinels and alarms of our wild kindred. Most inferior are our own abilities in using eyes, nose, and ears, when compared with the same functions in birds and animals.

Eyes and noses are important keys to the bright colours of birds and comparative sombreness of hairy-coated creatures. Take a dog and an oriole as good examples of the two extremes. When a dog has lost his master, he first looks about; then he strains his eyes with the intense look of a near-sighted person, and after a few moments of this he usually yelps with disappointment, drops his nose to the ground, and with unfailing accuracy follows the track of his master. When the freshness of the trail tells him that he is near its end he again resorts to his eyes, and is soon near enough to recognise the face he seeks. A fox when running before a hound may double back, and make a close reconnaissance near his trail, sometimes passing in full view without the hound's seeing him or stopping in following out the full curve of the trail, so completely does the wonderful power of smell absorb the entire attention of the dog.

Let us now turn to the oriole. As we might

infer, the nostrils incased in horn render the sense of smell of but slight account. It is hard to tell how much a bird can distinguish in this way— probably only the odour of food near at hand. However, when we examine the eye of our bird, we see a sense organ of a very high order. Bright, intelligent, full-circled, of great size compared to the bulk of the skull, protected by three complete eyelids; we realise that this must play an important part in the life of the bird. There are, of course, many exceptions to such a generalisation as this. For instance, many species of sparrows are dull-coloured. We must remember that the voice—the calls and songs of birds—is developed to a high degree, and in many instances renders bright colouring needless in attracting a mate or in locating a young bird.

As we have seen, the sense of smell is very highly developed among four-footed animals, but to make this efficient there must be something for it to act upon; and in this connection we find some interesting facts of which, outside of scientific books, little has been written. On the entire body, birds have only one gland—the oil gland above the base of the tail, which supplies an unctuous dressing for the feathers. Birds, therefore, have not the power of perspiring, but compensate for this by very rapid breathing. On the contrary, four-footed animals have glands on many portions of the body. Nature is seldom contented with the one primary function which an organ or tissue performs, but adjusts and adapts it to others in many ingenious ways. Hence, when an animal perspires, the pores of the skin allow the contained moisture to escape and moisten the surface of the body; but in addition to this, in many animals, collections of these pores in the shape of large glands secrete various odours which serve important uses. In the skunk such a gland is a practically perfect protection against attacks from his enemies. He never hurries and seems not to know what fear is—a single wave of his conspicuous danger signal is sufficient to clear his path.

In certain species of the rhinoceros there are large glands in the foot. These animals live among grass and herbage which they brush against as they walk, and thus "blaze" a plain trail for the mate or young to follow. There are few if any animals which care to face a rhinoceros, so the scent is incidentally useful to other creatures as a warning.

It is believed that the hard callosities on the legs of horses are the remains of glands which were once upon a time useful to their owners; and it is said that if a paring from one of these hard, horny structures be held to the nose of a horse, he will follow it about, hinting, perhaps, that in former days the scent from the gland was an instinctive guide which kept members of the herd together.

"Civet," which is obtained from the civet cat, and "musk," from the queer little hornless musk deer, are secretions of glands. It has been suggested that the defenceless musk deer escapes many of its enemies by the similarity of its secretion to the musky odour of crocodiles. In many animals which live together in herds, such as the antelope and deer, and which have neither bright colours nor far-reaching calls to aid straying members to regain the flock, there are large and active scent glands. The next time you see a live antelope in a zoological park, or even a stuffed specimen, look closely at the head, and between the eye and the nostril a large opening will be seen on each side, which, in the living animal, closes now and then, a flap of skin shutting it tight.

Among pigs the fierce peccary is a very social animal, going in large packs; and on the back of each of these creatures is found a large gland from which a clear watery fluid is secreted. Dogs and wolves also have their odour-secreting glands on the back, and the "wolf-pack" is proverbial.

The gland of the elephant is on the temple, and secretes only when the animal is in a dangerous mood, a hint, therefore, of opposite significance to that of the herding animals, as this says, "Let

me alone! stay away!'' Certain low species of
monkeys, the lemurs, have a remarkable bare
patch on the forearm, which covers a gland serving some use.

If we marvel at the keenness of scent among
animals, how incredible seems the similar sense
in insects—similar in function, however different
the medium of structure may be. Think of the
scent from a female moth, so delicate that we
cannot distinguish it, attracting a male of the
same species from a distance of a mile or more.
Entomologists sometimes confine a live female
moth or other insect in a small wire cage and
hang it outdoors in the evening, and in a short
time reap a harvest of gay-winged suitors which
often come in scores, instinctively following up
the trail of the delicate, diffused odour. It is
surely true that the greatest wonders are not
always associated with mere bulk.

INSECT MUSIC

AMONG insects, sounds are produced in many ways, and for various reasons. A species of ant which makes its nest on the under side of leaves produces a noise by striking the leaf with its head in a series of spasmodic taps, and another ant is also very interesting as regards its sound-producing habit. "Individuals of this species are sometimes spread over a surface of two square yards, many out of sight of the others; yet the tapping is set up at the same moment, continued exactly the same space of time, and stopped at the same instant. After the lapse of a few seconds, all recommence simultaneously. The interval is always approximately of the same duration, and each ant does not beat synchronously with every other ant, but only like those in the same group, so the independent tappings play a sort of tune, each group alike in time, but the tapping of the whole mass beginning and ending at the same instant. This is doubtless a means of communication."

The organ of hearing in insects is still to be discovered in many forms, but in katydids it is situated on the middle of the fore-legs; in butterflies on the sides of the thorax, while the tip of the horns or antennæ of many insects is considered to be the seat of this function. In all it is little more than a cavity, over which a skin is stretched like a drum-head, which thus reacts to the vibration. This seems to be very often "tuned," as it were, to the sounds made by the particular species in which it is found. A cricket will at times be unaffected by any sound, however loud, while at the slightest "screek" or chirp of its own species, no matter how faint, it will start its own little tune in all excitement.

The songs of the cicadas are noted all over the world. Darwin heard them while anchored half a mile off the South American coast, and a giant species of that country is said to produce a noise as loud as the whistle of a locomotive. Only the males sing, the females being dumb, thus giving rise to the well-known Grecian couplet:

> "Happy the cicadas' lives,
> For they all have voiceless wives."

Anyone who has entered a wood where thousands of the seventeen-year cicadas were hatching has never forgotten it. A threshing machine, or a gigantic frog chorus, is a fair comparison, and when a branch loaded with these insects is shaken, the sound rises to a shrill screech or scream. This noise is supposed—in fact is definitely known—to attract the female insect, and although there may be in it some tender notes which we fail to distinguish, yet let us hope that the absence of any highly organised auditory organ may result in reducing the effect of a steam-engine whistle to an agreeable whisper! It is thought that the vibrations are felt rather than heard, in the sense that we use the word "hear"; if one has ever had a cicada *zizz* in one's hand, the electrical shocks which seem to go up the arm help the belief in this idea. To many of us the song of the cicada—softened by distance—will ever be pleasant on account of its associations. When one attempts to picture a hot August day in a hay-field or along a dusty road, the drowsy *zee-ing* of this insect, growing louder and more accelerated and then as gradually dying away, is a focus for the mind's eye, around which the other details instantly group themselves.

The apparatus for producing this sound is one of the most complex in all the animal kingdom. In brief, it consists of two external doors, capable of being partly opened, and three internal membranes, to one of which is attached a vibrating muscle, which, put in motion, sets all the others vibrating in unison.

We attach a great deal of importance to the fact of being educated to the appreciation of the highest class of music. We applaud our Paderewski, and year after year are awed and delighted with wonderful operatic music, yet seldom is the *limitation* of human perception of musical sounds considered.

If we wish to appreciate the limits within which the human ear is capable of distinguishing sounds, we should sit down in a meadow, some hot mid-summer day, and listen to the subdued running murmur of the myriads of insects. Many are very distinct to our ears and we have little trouble in tracing them to their source. Such are crickets and grasshoppers, which fiddle and rasp their roughened hind legs against their wings. Some butterflies have the power of making a sharp crackling sound by means of hooks on the wings. The katydid, so annoying to some in its persistent ditty, so full of reminiscences to others of us, is a large, green, fiddling grasshopper.

Another sound which is typical of summer is the hum of insects' wings, sometimes, as near a beehive, rising to a subdued roar. The higher, thinner song of the mosquito's wings is unfortunately familiar to us, and we must remember that the varying tone of the hum of each species may be of the greatest importance to it as a means of recognition. Many beetles have a projecting horn on the under side of the body which they can snap against another projection, and by this means call their lady-loves, literally "playing the bones" in their minstrel serenade.

Although we can readily distinguish the sounds which these insects produce, yet there are hundreds of small creatures, and even large ones, which are provided with organs of hearing, but whose language is too fine for our coarse perceptions. The vibrations—chirps, hums, and clicks—can be recorded on delicate instruments, but, just as there are shades and colours at both ends of the spectrum which our eyes cannot perceive, so there are tones running we know not how far beyond the scale limits which affect our ears. Some creatures utter noises so shrill, so sharp, that it pains our ears to listen to them, and these are probably on the borderland of our sound-world.

Pipe, little minstrels of the waning year,
    In gentle concert pipe!
Pipe the warm noons; the mellow harvest near;
    The apples dropping ripe;

.   .   .   .:

The sweet sad hush on Nature's gladness laid;
    The sounds through silence heard!
Pipe tenderly the passing of the year.
                    HARRIET McEWEN KIMBALL.

I love to hear thine earnest voice,
    Wherever thou art hid,
Thou testy little dogmatist,
    Thou pretty Katydid!
Thou mindest me of gentlefolks,—
    Old gentlefolks are they,—
Thou say'st an undisputed thing
    In such a solemn way.
                    OLIVER WENDELL HOLMES.

AUGUST

THE GRAY DAYS OF BIRDS

THE temptation is great, if we love flowers, to pass over the seed time, when stalks are dried and leaves are shrivelled, no matter how beautiful may be the adaptation for scattering or preserving the seed or how wonderful the protective coats guarding against cold or wet. Or if insects attract us by their many varied interests, we are more enthusiastic over the glories of the full-winged imago than the less conspicuous, though no less interesting, eggs and chrysalides hidden away in crevices throughout the long winter.

Thus there seems always a time when we hesitate to talk or write of our favourite theme, especially if this be some class of life on the earth, because, perchance, it is not at its best.

Even birds have their gray days, when in the autumn the glory of their plumage and song has diminished. At this time few of their human admirers intrude upon them and the birds themselves are only too glad to escape observation. Collectors of skins disdain to ply their trade, as the ragged, pin-feathery coats of the birds now make sorry-looking specimens. But we can find something of interest in birddom, even in this interim.

Nesting is over, say you, when you start out on your tramps in late summer or early autumn; but do not be too sure. The gray purse of the oriole has begun to ravel at the edges and the haircloth cup of the chipping sparrow is already wind-distorted, but we shall find some housekeeping just begun.

The goldfinch is one of these late nesters. Long after his northern cousins, the pine siskins and snowflakes, have laid their eggs and reared their young, the goldfinch begins to focus the aerial loops of his flight about some selected spot and to collect beakfuls of thistledown. And here, perhaps, we have his fastidious reason for delaying. Thistles seed with the goldenrod, and not until this fleecy substance is gray and floating does he consider that a suitable nesting material is available.

When the young birds are fully fledged one would think the goldfinch a polygamist, as we see him in shining yellow and black, leading his family quintet, all sombre hued, his patient wife being to our eyes indistinguishable from the youngsters.

But in the case of most of the birds the cares of nesting are past, and the woods abound with full-sized but awkward young birds, blundering through their first month of insect-hunting and fly-catching, tumbling into the pools from which they try to drink, and shrieking with the very joy of

life, when it would be far safer for that very life
if they remained quiet.

It is a delightful period this, a transition as
interesting as evanescent. This is the time when
instinct begins to be aided by intelligence, when
every hour accumulates fact upon fact, all helping
to co-ordinate action and desire on the part of the
young birds.

No hint of migration has yet passed over the
land, and the quiet of summer still reigns; but
even as we say this a confused chuckling is heard;
this rises into a clatter of harsh voices, and a
small flock of blackbirds—two or three families—
pass overhead. The die is cast! No matter how
hot may be the sunshine during succeeding days,
or how contented and thoughtless of the future the
birds may appear, there is a something which has
gone, and which can never return until another
cycle of seasons has passed.

During this transition time some of our friends
are hardly recognisable; we may surprise the
scarlet tanager in a plumage which seems more
befitting a nonpareil bunting,—a regular "Jos-
eph's coat." The red of his head is half replaced
with a ring of green, and perhaps a splash of
the latter decorates the middle of his back. When
he flies the light shows through his wings in two
long narrow slits, where a pair of primaries are
lacking. It is a wise provision of Nature which
regulates the moulting sequence of his flight

feathers, so that only a pair shall fall out at one time, and the adjoining pair not before the new feathers are large and strong. A sparrow or oriole hopping along the ground with angular, half-naked wings would be indeed a pitiful sight, except to marauding weasels and cats, who would find meals in abundance on every hand.

Let us take our way to some pond or lake, thick with duckweed and beloved of wild fowl, and we shall find a different state of affairs. We surprise a group of mallard ducks, which rush out from the overhanging bank and dive for safety among the sheltering green arrowheads. But their out-spread wings are a mockery, the flight feathers showing as a mere fringe of quill sticks, which beat the water helplessly.

Another thing we notice. Where are the re-splendent drakes? Have they flown elsewhere and left their mates to endure the dangers of moulting alone? Let us come here a week later and see what a transformation is taking place. When most birds moult it is for a period of several months, but these ducks have a partial fall moult which is of the greatest importance to them. When the wing feathers begin to loosen in their sockets an unfailing instinct leads these birds to seek out some secluded pond, where they patiently await the moult. The sprouting, blood-filled quills force out the old feathers, and the bird becomes a thing of the water, to swim and to dive, with no more power of flight than its pond companions, the turtles.

If, however, the drake should retain his iridescent head and snowy collar, some sharp-eyed danger would spy out his helplessness and death would swoop upon him. So for a time his bright feathers fall out and a quick makeshift disguise closes over him—the reed-hued browns and grays of his mate—and for a time the pair are hardly distinguishable. With the return of his power of flight comes renewed brightness, and the wild drake emerges from his seclusion on strong-feathered, whistling wings. All this we should miss, did we not seek him out at this season; otherwise the few weeks would pass and we should notice no change from summer to winter plumage, and attribute his temporary absence to a whim of wandering on distant feeding grounds.

Another glance at our goldfinch shows a curious sight. Mottled with spots and streaks, yellow alternating with greenish, he is an anomaly indeed, and in fact all of our birds which undergo a radical colour change will show remarkable combinations during the actual process.

It is during the gray days that the secret to a great problem may be looked for—the why of migration.

A young duck of the year, whose wings are at

last strong and fit, waves them in ecstasy, vibrating from side to side and end to end of his natal pond. Then one day we follow his upward glances to where a thin, black arrow is throbbing southward, so high in the blue sky that the individual ducks are merged into a single long thread. The young bird, calling again and again, spurns the water with feet and wings, finally rising in a slowly ascending arc. Somewhere, miles to the southward, another segment approaches—touches —merges.

But what of our smaller birds? When the gray days begin to chill we may watch them hopping among the branches all day in their search for insects—a keener search now that so many of the more delicate flies and bugs have fallen chilled to the earth. Toward night the birds become more restless, feed less, wander aimlessly about, but, as we can tell by their chirps, remain near us until night has settled down. Then the irresistible maelstrom of migration instinct draws them upward,—upward,—climbing on fluttering wings, a mile or even higher into the thin air, and in company with thousands and tens of thousands they drift southward, sending vague notes down, but themselves invisible to us, save when now and then a tiny black mote floats across the face of the moon—an army of feathered mites, passing from tundra and spruce to bayou and palm.

In the morning, instead of the half-hearted

warble of an insect eater, there sounds in our ears, like the ring of skates on ice, the metallic, whip-like chirp of a snowbird, confident of his winter's seed feast.

LIVES OF THE LANTERN BEARERS

TO all wild creatures fire is an unknown and hated thing, although it is often so fascinating to them that they will stand transfixed gazing at its mysterious light, while a hunter, unnoticed, creeps up behind and shoots them.

In the depth of the sea, where the sun is powerless to send a single ray of light and warmth, there live many strange beings, fish and worms, which, by means of phosphorescent spots and patches, may light their own way. Of these strange sea folk we know nothing except from the fragments which are brought to the surface by the dredge; but over our fields and hedges, throughout the summer nights, we may see and study most interesting examples of creatures which produce their own light. Heedless of whether the moon shines brightly, or whether an overcast sky cloaks the blackest of nights, the fireflies blaze their sinuous path through life. These little yellow and black beetles, which illumine our way like a cloud of tiny meteors, have indeed a wonderful power, for the light which they produce within their own bodies is a cold glow, totally different from any fire of human agency.

In some species there seems to be a most romantic reason for their brilliance. Down among the grass blades are lowly, wingless creatures—the female fireflies, which, as twilight falls, leave their earthen burrows in the turf and, crawling slowly to the summit of some plant, they display the tiny lanterns which Nature has kindled within their bodies.

Far overhead shoot the strong-winged males, searching for their minute insect food, weaving glowing lines over all the shadowy landscape, and apparently heedless of all beneath them. Yet when the dim little beacon, hung out with the hopefulness of instinct upon the grass blade, is seen, all else is forgotten and the beetle descends to pay court to the poor, worm-like creature, so unlike him in appearance, but whose little illumination is her badge of nobility. The gallant suitor is as devoted as if the object of his affection were clad in all the gay colours of a butterfly; and he is fortunate if, when he has reached the signal among the grasses, he does not find a half-dozen firefly rivals before him.

When insects seek their mates by day, their characteristic colours or forms may be confused with surrounding objects; or those which by night are able in that marvellous way to follow the faintest scent up wind may have difficulties when cross currents of air are encountered; but the female firefly, waiting patiently upon her lowly leaf, has unequalled opportunity for winning her mate, for there is nothing to compare with or eclipse her flame. Except—I wonder if ever a firefly has hastened downward toward the strange glow which we sometimes see in the heart of decayed wood,—mistaking a patch of fox-fire for the love-light of which he was in search!

In other species, including the common one about our homes, the lady lightning-bug is more fortunate in possessing wings and is able to fly abroad like her mate.

Although this phosphorescence has been microscopically examined, it is but slightly understood. We know, however, that it is a wonderful process of combustion,—by which a bright light is produced without heat, smoke, or indeed fuel, except that provided by the life processes in the tiny body of the insect.

So shines a good deed in a naughty world.
SHAKESPEARE.

A STARFISH AND A DAISY

DAY after day the forms of horses, dogs, birds, and other creatures pass before our eyes. We look at them and call them by the names which we have given them, and yet—we see them not. That is to say, we say that they have a head, a tail; they run or fly; they are of one colour beneath, another above, but beyond these bare meaningless facts most of us never go.

Let us think of the meaning of form. Take, for example, a flower—a daisy. Now, if we could imagine such an impossible thing as that a daisy blossom should leave its place of growth, creep down the stem and go wandering off through the grass, soon something would probably happen to its shape. It would perhaps get in the habit of creeping with some one ray always in front, and the friction of the grass stems on either side would soon wear and fray the ends of the side rays, while those behind might grow longer and longer. If we further suppose that this strange daisy flower did not like the water, the rays in front might be of service in warning it to turn aside. When their tips touched the surface and were wet by the water of some pool, the ambulatory blossom would draw back and start out in a new direction. Thus a theoretical head (with the beginnings of the organs of sense), and a long-drawn-out tail, would have their origin.

Such a remarkable simile is not as fanciful as it might at first appear; for although we know of no blossom which so sets at naught the sedentary life of the vegetable kingdom, yet among certain of the animals which live their lives beneath the waves of the sea a very similar thing occurs.

Many miles inland, even on high mountains, we may sometimes see thousands of little joints, or bead-like forms, imbedded in great rocky cliffs. They have been given the name of St. Cuthbert's beads. Occasionally in the vicinity of these fossils—for such they are—are found impressions of a graceful, flower-like head, with many delicately divided petals, fixed forever in the hard relief of stone. The name of stone lilies has been applied to them. The beads were once strung together in the form of a long stem, and at the top the strangely beautiful animal-lily nodded its head in the currents of some deep sea, which in the long ago of the earth's age covered the land—millions of years before the first man or beast or bird drew breath.

It was for a long time supposed that these wonderful creatures were extinct, but dredges have brought up from the dark depths of the sea actual living stone lilies, or *crinoids,* this being their real name. Few of us will probably ever have an opportunity of studying a crinoid alive, although in our museums we may see them preserved in glass jars. That, however, detracts nothing from the marvel of their history and relationship. They send root-like organs deep into the mud, where they coil about some shell and there cling fast. Then the stem grows tall and slender, and upon the summit blooms or is developed the animal-flower. Its nourishment is not drawn from the roots and the air, as is that of the daisy, but is provided by the tiny creatures which swim to its tentacles, or are borne thither by the ocean currents. Some of these crinoids, as if impatient of their plant-like life and asserting their animal kinship, at last tear themselves free from their stem and float off, turn over, and thereafter live happily upon the bottom of the sea, roaming where they will, creeping slowly along and fulfilling the destiny of our imaginary daisy.

And here a comparison comes suddenly to mind. How like to a many-rayed starfish is our creeping crinoid! Few of us, unless we had studies about these creatures, could distinguish between a crinoid and one of the frisky little dancing stars, or serpent stars, which are so common in the rocky caves along our coast. This relationship is no less real than apparent. The hard-skinned "five finger," or common starfish, which we may pick up on any beach, while it never grew upon a stem, yet still preserves the radial symmetry of its stalked ancestors. Pick up your starfish, carry it to the nearest field, and pluck a daisy close to the head. How interesting the comparison becomes, now that the knowledge of its meaning is plain. Anything which grows fast upon a single immovable stem tends to grow equally in all directions. We need not stop here, for we may include sea anemones and corals, those most marvellously coloured flowers of the sea, which grow upon a short, thick stalk and send out their tentacles equally in all directions. And many of the jellyfish which throb along close beneath the surface swells were in their youth each a section of a pile of saucer-like individuals, which were fastened by a single stalk to some shell or piece of coral.

We will remember that it was suggested that the theoretical daisy would soon alter its shape after it entered upon active life. This is plainly seen in the starfish, although at first glance the creature seems as radially symmetrical as a wheel. But at one side of the body, between two of the arms, is a tiny perforated plate, serving to strain the water which enters the body, and thus the circular tendency is broken, and a beginning made toward right and left handedness. In certain sea-urchins, which are really starfishes with the gaps between the arms filled up, the body is elongated, and thus the head and tail conditions of all animals higher in the scale of life are represented.

THE DREAM OF THE YELLOW-THROAT

MANY of us look with longing to the days of Columbus; we chafe at the thought of no more continents to discover; no unknown seas to encompass. But at our very doors is an "undiscovered bourne," from which, while the traveller invariably returns, yet he will have penetrated but slightly into its mysteries. This unexplored region is night.

When the dusk settles down and the creatures of sunlight seek their rest, a new realm of life awakens into being. The flaring colours and loud bustle of the day fade and are lost, and in their place come soft, gray tones and silence. The scarlet tanager seeks some hidden perch and soon from the same tree slips a silent, ghostly owl; the ruby of the hummingbird dies out as the gaudy flowers of day close their petals, and the gray wraiths of sphinx moths appear and sip nectar from the spectral moonflowers.

.   .   .   .

With feet shod with silence, let us creep near a dense tangle of sweetbrier and woodbine late some summer evening and listen to the sounds of the night-folk. How few there are that our ears can

analyse! We huddle close to the ground and shut
our eyes. Then little by little we open them and
set our senses of sight and hearing at keenest
pitch. Even so, how handicapped are we compared to the wild creatures. A tiny voice becomes
audible, then dies away,—entering for a moment
the narrow range of our coarse hearing,—and
finishing its message of invitation or challenge in
vibrations too fine for our ears.

．　．　．　．　．　．　．

Were we crouched by a dense yew hedge, bordering an English country lane, a nightingale
might delight us,—a melody of day, softened,
adapted, to the night. If the air about us was
heavy with the scent of orange blossoms of some
covert in our own southland, the glorious harmony
of a mocking-bird might surge through the gloom,
—assuaging the ear as do the blossoms another
sense.

But sitting still in our own home tangle let us
listen,—listen. Our eyes have slipped the scales
of our listless civilised life and pierce the darkness with the acuteness of our primeval forefathers; our ears tingle and strain.

A slender tongue of sound arises from the bush
before us. Again and again it comes, muffled but
increasing in volume. A tiny ball of feathers is
perched in the centre of the tangle, with beak

hidden in the deep, soft plumage, but ever and anon the little body throbs and the song falls gently on the silence of the night: "I beseech you! I beseech you! I beseech you!" A Maryland yellow-throat is asleep and singing in its dreams.

As we look and listen, a shadowless something hovers overhead, and, looking upward, we see a gray screech owl silently hanging on beating wings. His sharp ears have caught the muffled sound; his eyes search out the tangle, but the yellow-throat is out of reach. The little hunter drifts away into the blackness, the song ends and the sharp squeak of a mouse startles us. We rise slowly from our cramped position and quietly leave the mysteries of the night.

SEPTEMBER

THE PASSING OF THE FLOCKS

IT is September. August—the month of gray days for birds—has passed. The last pinfeather of the new winter plumage has burst its sheath, and is sleek and glistening from its thorough oiling with waterproof dressing, which the birds squeeze out with their bills from a special gland, and which they rub into every part of their plumage. The youngsters, now grown as large as their parents, have become proficient in fly-catching or berry-picking, as the case may be. Henceforth they forage for themselves, although if we watch carefully we may still see a parent's love prompting it to give a berry to its big offspring (indistinguishable save for this attention), who greedily devours it without so much as a wing flutter of thanks.

Two courses are open to the young birds who have been so fortunate as to escape the dangers of nestlinghood. They may unite in neighbourly flocks with others of their kind, as do the blackbirds of the marshes; or they may wander off by themselves, never going very far from their summer home, but perching alone each night in the thick foliage of some sheltering bush.

How wonderfully the little fellow adapts himself to the radical and sudden change in his life!

Before this, his world has been a warm, soft-lined nest, with ever anxious parents to shelter him from rain and cold, or to stand with half-spread wings between him and the burning rays of the sun. He has only to open his mouth and call for food and a supply of the choicest morsels appears and is shoved far down his throat. If danger threatens, both parents are ready to fight to the last, or even willing to give their lives to protect him. Little wonder is it that the young birds are loth to leave; we can sympathise heart-ily with the last weaker brother, whose feet cling convulsively to the nest, who begs piteously for "just one more caterpillar!" But the mother bird is inexorable and stands a little way out of reach with the juiciest morsel she can find. Once out, the young bird never returns. Even if we catch the little chap before he finishes his first flight and replace him, the magic spell of home is broken, and he is out again the instant our hand frees him.

What a change the first night brings! Yet with unfailing instinct he squats on some twig, fluffs up his feathers, tucks his wee head behind his wing, and sleeps the sleep of his first adult birdhood as soundly as if this position of rest had been familiar to him since he broke through the shell.

We admire his aptitude for learning; how quickly his wings gain strength and skill; how soon he manages to catch his own dinner. But how all this pales before the accomplishment of a young brush turkey or moundbuilder of the antipodes. Hatched six or eight feet under ground, merely by the heat of decaying vegetation, no fond parents minister to his wants. Not only must he escape from the shell in the pressure and darkness of his underground prison (how we cannot tell), but he is then compelled to dig through six feet of leaves and mould before he reaches the sunlight. He finds himself well feathered, and at once spreads his small but perfect wings and goes humming off to seek his living alone and unattended.

It is September—the month of restlessness for the birds. Weeks ago the first migrants started on their southward journey, the more delicate insect-eaters going first, before the goldfinches and other late nesters had half finished housekeeping. The northern warblers drift past us southward—the magnolia, blackburnian, Canadian fly-catching, and others, bringing memories of spruce and balsam to those of us who have lived with them in the forests of the north.

"It's getting too cold for the little fellows," says the wiseacre, who sees you watching the smaller birds as they pass southward. Is it, though? What of the tiny winter wren which spends the zero weather with us? His coat is no warmer than those birds which have gone to the far tropics. And what of the flocks of birds which we occasionally come across in mid-winter, of species which generally migrate to Brazil? It is not the cold which deprives us of our summer friends, or at least the great majority of them; it is the decrease in food supply. Insects disappear, and only those birds which feed on seeds and buds, or are able to glean an insect diet from the crevices of fence and tree-trunk, can abide.

This is the month to climb out on the roof of your house, lie on your back and listen. He is a stolid person indeed who is not moved by the chirps and twitters which come down through the darkness. There is no better way to show what a wonderful power sound has upon our memories. There sounds a robin's note, and spring seems here again; through the night comes a white-throat's chirp, and we see again the fog-dimmed fields of a Nova Scotian upland; a sandpiper "peets" and the scene in our mind's eye as instantly changes, and so on. What a revelation if we could see as in daylight for a few moments! The sky would be pitted with thousands and thousands of birds flying from a few hundred yards to as high as one or two miles above the earth.

It only adds to the interest of this phenomenon when we turn to our learned books on birds for an explanation of the origin of migration, the whence and whither of the long journeys by day and night, and find—no certain answer! This is one of the greatest of the many mysteries of the natural world, of which little is known, although much is guessed, and the bright September nights may reveal to us—we know not what undiscovered facts.

> I see my way as birds their trackless way.
> I shall arrive; what time, what circuit first,
> I ask not; but unless God sends his hail
> Of blinding fire-balls, sleet or driving snow,
> In sometime, his good time, I shall arrive;
> He guides me and the bird. In his good time.
>   ROBERT BROWNING.

GHOSTS OF THE EARTH

WE may know the name of every tree near our home; we may recognise each blossom in the field, every weed by the wayside; yet we should be astonished to be told that there are hundreds of plants—many of them of exquisite beauty—which we have overlooked in very sight of our doorstep. What of the green film which is drawn over every moist tree-trunk or shaded wall, or of the emerald film which coats the water of the pond's edge? Or the gray lichens painting the rocks and logs, toning down the shingles; the toadstools which, like pale vegetable ghosts, spring up in a night from the turf; or the sombre puff balls which seem dead from their birth?

The moulds which cover bread and cheese with a delicate tracery of filaments and raise on high their tiny balls of spores are as worthy to be called a plant growth as are the great oaks which shade our houses. The rusts and mildews and blights which destroy our fruit all have their beauty of growth and fruition when we examine them through a lens, and the yeast by which flour and water is made to rise into the porous, spongy dough is just as truly a plant as is the geranium blossoming at the kitchen window.

If we wonder at the fierce struggle for existence

which allows only a few out of the many seeds of a maple or thistle to germinate and grow up, how can we realise the obstacles with which these lowly plants have to contend? A weed in the garden may produce from one to ten thousand seeds, and one of our rarest ferns scatters in a single season over fifty millions spores; while from the larger puff-balls come clouds of unnumbered millions of spores, blowing to the ends of the earth; yet we may search for days without finding one full-grown individual.

All the assemblage of mushrooms and toad-stools,—although the most deadly may flaunt bright hues of scarlet and yellow,—yet lack the healthy green of ordinary plants. This is due to the fact that they have become brown parasites or scavengers, and instead of transmuting heat and moisture and the salts of the earth into tissue by means of the pleasant-hued chlorophyll, these sylvan ghosts subsist upon the sap of roots or the tissues of decaying wood. Emancipated from the normal life of the higher plants, even flowers have been denied them and their fruit is but a cloud of brown dust,—each mote a simple cell.

But what of the delicate Indian pipe which gleams out from the darkest aisles of the forest? If we lift up its hanging head we will find a per-fect flower, and its secret is discovered. Traitor to its kind, it has dropped from the ranks of the laurels, the heather, and the jolly little wintergreens to the colourless life of a parasite,—hob-nobbing with clammy toadstools and slimy lichens. Its common names are all appropriate,—ice-plant, ghost-flower, corpse-plant.

Nevertheless it is a delicately beautiful creation, and we have no right to apply our human standards of ethics to these children of the wild, whose only chance of life is to seize every opportunity,—to make use of each hint of easier existence.

We have excellent descriptions and classifications of mushrooms and toadstools, but of the actual life of these organisms, of the conditions of their growth, little is known. Some of the most hideous are delicious to our palate, some of the most beautiful are certain death. The splendid red and yellow amanita, which lights up a dark spot in the woods like some flowering orchid, is a veritable trap of death. Though human beings have learned the fatal lesson and leave it alone, the poor flies in the woods are ever deceived by its brightness, or odour, and a circle of their bodies upon the ground shows the result of their ignorance.

MUSKRATS

LONG before man began to inherit the earth, giant beavers built their dams and swam in the streams of long ago. For ages these creatures have been extinct. Our forefathers, during historical times, found smaller beavers abundant, and with such zeal did they trap them that this modern race is now well-nigh vanished. Nothing is left to us but the humble muskrat,—which in name and in facile adaptation to the encroachments of civilization has little in common with his more noble predecessor. Yet in many ways his habits of life bring to mind the beaver.

Let us make the most of our heritage and watch at the edge of a stream some evening in late fall. If the muskrats have half finished their mound of sticks and mud, which is to serve them for a winter home, we will be sure to see some of them at work. Two lines of ripples furrow the surface outward from the farther bank, and a small dark form clambers upon the pile of rubbish. Suddenly a *spat!* sounds at our very feet, and a muskrat dives headlong into the water, followed by the one on the ground. Another *spat!* and splash comes from farther down the stream, and so the danger signal of the muskrat clan is

passed along,—a single flap upon the water with
the flat of the tail.

.   .   .   .

If we wait silent and patient, the work will be
taken up anew, and in the pale moonlight the
little labourers will fashion their house, lining
the upper chamber with soft grasses, and shaping
the steep passageway which will lead to the ever-
unfrozen stream-bed. Either here or in the snug
tunnel nest deep in the bank the young muskrats
are born, and here they are weaned upon toothsome mussels and succulent lily roots.

Safe from all save mink and owl and trap, these
sturdy muskrats spend the summer in and about
the streams; and when winter shuts down hard
and fast, they live lives more interesting than any
of our other animals. The ground freezes their
tunnels into tubes of iron,—the ice seals the
surface, past all gnawing out; and yet, amid the
quietly flowing water, where snow and wind never
penetrate, these warm-blooded, air-breathing
muskrats live the winter through, with only the
trout and eels for company. Their food is the
bark and pith of certain plants; their air is what
leaks through the house of sticks, or what may
collect at the melting-place of ice and shore.

Stretched full length on the smooth ice, let us
look through into that strange nether world,

where the stress of storm is unknown. Far beneath us sinuous black forms undulate through the water,—from tunnel to house and back again. As we gaze down through the crystalline mass, occasional fractures play pranks with the objects below. The animate shapes seem to take unto themselves greater bulk; their tails broaden, their bodies become many times longer. For a moment the illusion is perfect; thousands of centuries have slipped back, and we are looking at the giant beavers of old.

Let us give thanks that even the humble muskrat still holds his own. A century or two hence and posterity may look with wonder at his stuffed skin in a museum!

NATURE'S GEOMETRICIANS

SPIDERS form good subjects for a rainy-day study, and two hours spent in a neglected garret watching these clever little beings will often arouse such interest that we shall be glad to devote many days of sunshine to observing those species which hunt and build, and live their lives in the open fields. There is no insect in the world with more than six legs, and as a spider has eight he is therefore thrown out of the company of butterflies, beetles, and wasps and finds himself in a strange assemblage. Even to his nearest relatives he bears little resemblance, for when we realise that scorpions and horseshoe crabs must call him cousin, we perceive that his is indeed an aberrant bough on the tree of creation.

Leaving behind the old-fashioned horseshoe crabs to feel their way slowly over the bottom of the sea, the spiders have won for themselves on land a place high above the mites, ticks, and daddy-long-legs, and in their high development and intricate powers of resource they yield not even to the ants and bees.

Nature has provided spiders with an organ filled always with liquid which, on being exposed to the air, hardens, and can be drawn out into the slender threads we know as cobweb. The silkworm encases its body with a mile or more of gleaming silk, but there its usefulness is ended as far as the silkworm is concerned. But spiders have found a hundred uses for their cordage, some of which are startlingly similar to human inventions.

Those spiders which burrow in the earth hang their tunnels with silken tapestries impervious to wet, which at the same time act as lining to the tube. Then the entrance may be a trap-door of soil and silk, hinged with strong silken threads; or in the turret spiders which are found in our fields there is reared a tiny tower of leaves or twigs bound together with silk. Who of us has not teased the inmate by pushing a bent straw into his stronghold and awaiting his furious onslaught upon the innocent stalk!

A list of all the uses of cobwebs would take more space than we can spare; but of these the most familiar is the snare set for unwary flies,— the wonderfully ingenious webs which sparkle with dew among the grasses or stretch from bush to bush. The framework is of strong webbing and upon this is closely woven the sticky spiral which is so elastic, so ethereal, and yet strong enough to entangle a good-sized insect. How knowing seems the little worker, as when, the web and his den of concealment being completed, he spins a strong cable from the centre of the web to the entrance of his watch-tower. Then, when a trembling of his aerial spans warns him of a capture, how eagerly he seizes his master cable and jerks away on it, thus vibrating the whole structure and making more certain the confusion of his victim.

What is more interesting than to see a great yellow garden-spider hanging head downward in the centre of his web, when we approach too closely, instead of deserting his snare, set it vibrating back and forth so rapidly that he becomes a mere blur; a more certain method of escaping the onslaught of a bird than if he ran to the shelter of a leaf.

Those spiders which leap upon their prey instead of setting snares for it have still a use for their threads of life, throwing out a cable as they leap, to break their fall if they miss their foothold. What a strange use of the cobweb is that of the little flying spiders! Up they run to the top of a post, elevate their abdomens and run out several threads which lengthen and lengthen until the breeze catches them and away go the wingless aeronauts for yards or for miles as fortune and wind and weather may dictate! We wonder if they can cut loose or pull in their balloon cables at will.

Many species of spiders spin a case for holding their eggs, and some carry this about with them until the young are hatched.

A most fascinating tale would unfold could we discover all the uses of cobweb when the spiders

themselves are through with it. Certain it is that
our ruby-throated hummingbird robs many webs
to fasten together the plant down, wood pulp,
and lichens which compose her dainty nest.

Search the pond and you will find another member of the spider family swimming about at ease
beneath the surface, thoroughly aquatic in habits,
but breathing a bubble of air which he carries
about with him. When his supply is low he swims
to a submarine castle of silk, so air-tight that he
can keep it filled with a large bubble of air, upon
which he draws from time to time.

And so we might go on enumerating almost end-
less uses for the web which is Nature's gift to
these little waifs, who ages ago left the sea and
have won a place for themselves in the sunshine
among the butterflies and flowers.

.   .   .   .

In the balsam-perfumed shade of our northern
forests we may sometimes find growing in abundance the tiny white dwarf cornel, or bunch-berry,
as its later cluster of scarlet fruit makes the more
appropriate name. These miniature dogwood
blossoms (or imitation blossoms, as the white di-
visions are not real petals) are very conspicuous
against the dark moss, and many insects seem to
seek them out and to find it worth while to visit
them. If we look very carefully we may find that

this discovery is not original with us, for a little creature has long ago found out the fondness of bees and other insects for these flowers and has put his knowledge to good use.

One day I saw what I thought was a swelling on one part of the flower, but a closer look showed it was a living spider. Here was protective colouring carried to a wonderful degree. The body of the spider was white and glistening, like the texture of the white flower on which he rested. On his abdomen were two pink, oblong spots of the same tint and shape as the pinkened tips of the false petals. Only by an accident could he be discovered by a bird, and when I focussed my camera, I feared that the total lack of contrast would make the little creature all but invisible.

Confident with the instinct handed down through many generations, the spider trusted implicitly to his colour for safety and never moved, though I placed the lens so close that it threw a life-sized image on the ground-glass. When all was ready, and before I had pressed the bulb, the thought came to me whether this wonderful resemblance should be attributed to the need of escaping from insectivorous birds, or to the increased facility with which the spider would be able to catch its prey. At the very instant of making the exposure, before I could will the stopping of the movement of my fingers, if I had so wished, my question was answered. A small, iridescent, green bee flew down, like a spark of living light, upon the flower, and, quick as thought, was caught in the jaws of the spider. Six of his eight legs were not brought into use, but were held far back out of the way.

Here, on my lens, I had a little tragedy of the forest preserved for all time.

There was no bud, no bloom upon the bowers;
   The spiders wove their thin shrouds night by night;
The thistle-down, the only ghost of flowers,
   Sailed slowly by—passed noiseless out of sight.
                              THOMAS BUCHANAN READ.

OCTOBER

AUTUMN HUNTING WITH A FIELD GLASS

O NE of the most uncertain of months is October, and most difficult for the beginner in bird study. If we are just learning to enjoy the life of wood and field, we will find hard tangles to unravel among the birds of this month. Many of the smaller species which passed us on their northward journey last spring are now returning and will, perhaps, tarry a week or more before starting on the next nocturnal stage of their passage tropicward. Many are almost unrecognisable in their new winter plumage. Male scarlet tanagers are now green tanagers, goldfinches are olive finches, while instead of the beautiful black, white, and cream dress which made so easy the identification of the meadow bobolinks in the spring, search will now be rewarded only by some plump, overgrown sparrows—reedbirds—which are really bobolinks in disguise.

Orchard orioles and rose-breasted grosbeaks come and are welcomed, but the multitude of female birds of these species which appear may astonish one, until he discovers that the young birds, both male and female, are very similar to their mother in colour. We have no difficulty in distinguishing between adult bay-breasted and black poll warblers, but he is indeed a keen observer who can point out which is which when the young birds of the year pass.

October is apt to be a month of extremes. One day the woods are filled with scores of birds, and on the next hardly one will be seen. Often a single species or family will predominate, and one will remember "thrush days" or "woodpecker days." Yellow-bellied sapsuckers cross the path, flickers call and hammer in every grove, while in the orchards, and along the old worm-eaten fences, glimpses of red, white, and black show where red-headed woodpeckers are looping from trunk to post. When we listen to the warble of bluebirds, watch the mock courtship of the high-holders, and discover the fall violets under leaves and burrs, for an instant a feeling of spring rushes over us; but the yellow leaves blow against our face, the wind sighs through the cedars, and we realise that the black hand of the frost will soon end the brave efforts of the wild pansies.

The thrushes, ranking in some ways at the head of all our birds, drift through the woods, brown and silent as the leaves around them. Splendid opportunities they give us to test our powers of woodcraft. A thrush passes like a streak of brown light and perches on a tree some distance away. We creep from tree to tree, darting nearer when his head is turned. At last we think we are within range, and raise our weapon. No, a leaf is in the way, and the dancing spots of sunlight

make our aim uncertain. We move a little closer
and again take aim, and this time he cannot escape
us. Carefully our double-barrelled binoculars
cover him, and we get what powder and lead could
never give us—the quick glance of the hazel eye,
the trembling, half-raised feathers on his head,
and a long look at the beautifully rounded form
perched on the twig, which a wanton shot would
destroy forever. The rich rufous colouring of
the tail proclaims him a singer of singers—a hermit thrush. We must be on the watch these days
for the beautiful wood thrush, the lesser spotted
veery, the well named olive-back and the rarer
gray-cheeked thrush. We may look in vain among
the thrushes in our bird books for the golden-
crowned and water thrush, for these walkers of
the woods are thrushes only in appearance, and
belong to the family of warblers. The long-tailed
brown thrashers, lovers of the undergrowth, are
still more thrush-like in look, but in our classifications they hold the position of giant cousins to the
wrens. Even the finches contribute a mock thrush
to our list, the big, spotted-breasted fox sparrow,
but he rarely comes in number before mid October
or November. Of course we all know that our
robin is a true thrush, young robins having their
breasts thickly spotted with black, while even
the old birds retain a few spots and streaks on
the throat.

If we search behind the screen of leaves and

grass around us we may discover many tragedies. One fall I picked up a dead olive-backed thrush in the Zoological Park. There were no external signs of violence, but I found that the food canal was pretty well filled with blood. The next day still another bird was found in the same condition, and the day after two more. Within a week I noted in my journal eight of these thrushes, all young birds of the year, and all with the same symptoms of disorder. I could only surmise that some poisonous substance, some kind of berry, perhaps some attractive but deadly exotic from the Botanical Gardens, had tempted the inexperienced birds and caused their deaths.

As we walk through the October woods a covey of ruffed grouse springs up before us, overhead a flock of robins dashes by, and the birds scatter to feed among the wild grapes. The short round wings of the grouse whirr noisily, while the quick wing beats of the robins make little sound. Both are suited to their uses. The robin may travel league upon league to the south, while the grouse will not go far except to find new bud or berry pastures. His wings, as we have noticed before, are fitted rather for sudden emergencies, to bound up before the teeth of the fox close upon him, to dodge into close cover when the nose of the hound almost touches his trembling body. When he scrambled out of his shell last May he at once began to run about and to try his tiny wings, and little by little he taught himself to fly. But in the efforts he got many a tumble and broke or lost many a feather. Nature, however, has foreseen this, and to her grouse children she gives several changes of wing feathers to practise with, before the last strong winter quills come in.

How different it is with the robin. Naked and helpless he comes from his blue shell, and only one set of wing quills falls to his share, so it behooves him to be careful indeed of these. He remains in the nest until they are strong enough to bear him up, and his first attempts are carefully supervised by his anxious parents. And so the glimpse we had in the October woods of the two pair of wings held more of interest than we at first thought.

In many parts of the country, about October fifteenth the crows begin to flock back and forth to and from their winter roosts. In some years it is the twelfth, or again the seventeenth, but the constancy of the mean date is remarkable. Many of our winter visitants have already slipped into our fields and woods and taken the places of some of the earlier southern migrants; but the daily passing of the birds which delay their journey until fairly pinched by the lack of food at the first frosts extends well into November. It is not until the foliage on the trees and bushes becomes threadbare and the last migrants have flown, that our northern visitors begin to take a prominent place in our avifauna.

> Season of mists and mellow fruitfulness!
>   Close bosom friend of the maturing sun;
>
> Where are the songs of spring? Ay, where are they?
>   Think not of them, thou hast thy music too,—
> While barred clouds bloom the soft-dying day,
>   And touch the stubble-plains with rosy hue;
> Then in a wailful choir the small gnats mourn
>   Among the river-sallows, borne aloft
>   Or sinking as the light wind lives or dies;
> And full-grown lambs loud bleat from hilly bourn;
>   Hedge-crickets sing, and now with treble soft
>   The red-breast whistles from a garden-croft,
>   And gathering swallows twitter in the skies.
>   JOHN KEATS.

A WOODCHUCK AND A GREBE

NO fact comes to mind which is not more impressed upon us by the valuable aid of comparisons, and Nature is ever offering antitheses. At this season we are generally given a brief glimpse—the last for the year—of two creatures, one a mammal, the other a bird, which are as unlike in their activities as any two living creatures could well be.

What a type of lazy contentment is the woodchuck, as throughout the hot summer days he lies on his warm earthen hillock at the entrance of his burrow. His fat body seems almost to flow down the slope, and when he waddles around for a nibble of clover it is with such an effort that we feel sure he would prefer a comfortable slow starvation, were it not for the unpleasant feelings involved in such a proceeding.

As far as I know there are but two things which can rouse a woodchuck to strenuous activity; when a dog is in pursuit he can make his stumpy feet fairly twinkle as he flies for his burrow, and when a fox or a man is digging him out, he can literally worm his way through the ground, frequently escaping by means of his wonderful digging power. But when September or October days bring the first chill, he gives one last yawn upon the world and stows himself away at the farthest end of his tunnel, there to sleep away the winter. Little more does he know of the snows and blizzards than the bird which has flown to the tropics. Even storing up fruits or roots is too great an effort for the indolent woodchuck, and in his hibernation stupor he draws only upon the fat which his lethargic summer life has accumulated within his skin.

As we might expect from a liver of such a slothful life, the family traits of the woodchuck are far from admirable and there is said to be little affection shown by the mother woodchuck toward her young. The poor little fellows are pushed out of the burrow and driven away to shift for themselves as soon as possible. Many of them must come to grief from hawks and foxes. Closely related to the squirrels, these large marmots (for they are first cousins to the prairie dogs) are as unlike them in activity as they are in choice of a haunt.

What a contrast to all this is the trim feathered form which we may see on the mill pond some clear morning. Alert and wary, the grebe paddles slowly along, watchful of every movement. If we approach too closely, it may settle little by little, like a submarine opening its water compartments, until nothing is visible except the head with its sharp beak. Another step and the bird has vanished, swallowed up by the lake, and the chances are a hundred to one against our discovering the motionless neck and the tiny eye which rises again among the water weeds.

This little grebe comes of a splendid line of ancestors, some of which were even more specialised for an aquatic life. These paid the price of existence along lines too narrow and vanished from the earth. The grebe, however, has so far stuck to a life which bids fair to allow his race safety for many generations, but he is perilously near the limit. Every fall he migrates far southward, leaving his northern lakes, but if the water upon which he floats should suddenly dry up, he would be almost as helpless as the gasping fish; for his wings are too weak to lift him from the ground. He must needs have a long take-off, a flying start, aided by vigorous paddling along the surface of the water, before he can rise into the air.

Millions of years ago there lived birds built on the general grebe plan and who doubtless were derived from the same original stock, but which lived in the great seas of that time. Far from being able to migrate, every external trace of wing was gone and these great creatures, almost as large as a man and with sharp teeth in their beaks, must have hitched themselves like seals along the edge of the beach, and perhaps laid their eggs on the pebbles as do the terns to-day.

The grebe, denied the power to rise easily and

even to run about on land without considerable effort, is, however, splendidly adapted to its water life, and the rapidity of its motions places it near the head of the higher active creatures,—with the woodchuck near the opposite extreme.

THE VOICE OF ANIMALS

THROUGHOUT the depths of the sea, silence, as well as absolute darkness, prevails. The sun penetrates only a short distance below the surface, at most a few hundred feet, and all disturbance from storms ceases far above that depth. Where the pressure is a ton or more to the square inch, it is very evident that no sound vibration can exist. Near the surface it is otherwise. The majority of fishes have no lungs and of course no vocal chords, but certain species, such as the drumfish, are able to distend special sacs with gas or air, or in other ways to produce sounds. One variety succeeds in producing a number of sounds by gritting the teeth, and when the male fish is attempting to charm the female by dashing round her, spreading his fins to display his brilliant colours, this gritting of the teeth holds a prominent place in the performance, although whether the fair finny one makes her choice because she prefers a high-toned grit instead of a lower one can only be imagined! But vibrations, whether of sound or of water pressure, are easily carried near the surface, and fishes are provided with organs to receive and record them. One class of such organs has little in common with ears, as we speak of them; they are merely points on the head

and body which are susceptible to the watery
vibrations. These points are minute cavities, surrounded with tiny *cilia* or hairs, which connect
with the ends of the nerves.

The ears of the frogs and all higher animals
are, like the tongue-bone and the lower jaw,
derived originally from portions of gills, which
the aquatic ancestors of living animals used to
draw the oxygen from the water. This is one of
the most wonderful and interesting changes which
the study of evolution has unfolded to our
knowledge.

The disproportionate voices are produced by
means of an extra amount of skin on the throat,
which is distensible and acts as a drum to increase
the volume of sound. In certain bullfrogs which
grow to be as large as the head of a man, the bel-
lowing power is deafening and is audible for miles.
In Chile a small species of frog, measuring only
about an inch in length, has two internal vocal
sacs which are put to a unique use. Where these
frogs live, water is very scarce and the polliwogs
have no chance to live and develop in pools, as is
ordinarily the case. So when the eggs are laid,
they are immediately taken by the male frog and
placed in these capacious sacs, which serve as
nurseries for them all through their hatching and
growing period of life. Although there is no water in these chambers, yet their gills grow out and
are reabsorbed, just as is the case in ordinary

tadpoles. When their legs are fully developed, they clamber up to their father's broad mouth and get their first glimpse of the great world from his lower lip. When fifteen partly developed polliwogs are found in the pouches of one little frog, he looks as if he had gorged himself to bursting with tadpoles. To such curious uses may vocal organs be put.

Turtles are voiceless, except at the period of laying eggs, when they acquire a voice, which even in the largest is very tiny and piping, like some very small insect rather than a two-hundred-pound tortoise. Some of the lizards utter shrill, insect-like squeaks.

A species of gecko, a small, brilliantly coloured lizard, has the back of its tail armed with plates. These it has a habit of rubbing together, and by this means it produces a shrill, chirruping sound, which actually attracts crickets and grasshoppers toward the noise, so that they fall easy prey to this reptilian trapper. So in colour, sound, motion, and many other ways, animals act and react upon each other, a useful and necessary habit being perverted by an enemy, so that the death of the creature results. Yet it would never be claimed that the lizard thought out this mimicking. It probably found that certain actions resulted in the approach of good dinners, and in its offspring this action might be partly instinctive, and each generation would perpetuate it. If it had been an intentional act, other nearly related species of lizards would imitate it, as soon as they perceived the success which attended it.

That many animals have a kind of language is nowadays admitted to be a truism, but this is more evident among mammals and birds, and, reviewing the classes of the former, we find a more or less defined ascending complexity and increased number of varying sounds as we pass from the lower forms—kangaroos and moles—to the higher herb-and-flesh-eaters, and particularly monkeys.

Squeaks and grunts constitute the vocabulary, if we dignify it by that name, of the mammals. The sloths, those curious animals whose entire life is spent clinging to the underside of branches, on whose leaves they feed, may be said almost to be voiceless, so seldom do they give utterance to the nameless wail which constitutes their only utterance. Even when being torn to pieces by an enemy, they offer no resistance and emit no sound, but fold their claws around their body and submit to the inevitable as silently and as stoically as did ever an ancient Spartan.

Great fear of death will often cause an animal to utter sounds which are different from those produced under any other conditions. When an elephant is angry or excited, his trumpeting is terribly loud and shrill; but when a mother elephant is "talking" to her child, while the same sonorous, metallic quality is present, yet it is wonderfully softened and modulated. A horse is a good example of what the fear of death will do. The ordinary neigh of a horse is very familiar, but in battle when mortally wounded, or having lost its master and being terribly frightened, a horse will scream, and those who have heard it, say it is more awful than the cries of pain of a human being.

Deer and elk often astonish one by the peculiar sounds which they produce. An elk can bellow loudly, especially when fighting; but when members of a herd call to each other, or when surprised by some unusual appearance, they whistle —a sudden, sharp whistle, like the tin mouthpieces with revolving discs, which were at one time so much in evidence.

The growl of a bear differs greatly under varying circumstances. There is the playful growl, uttered when two individuals are wrestling, and the terrible "sound"—no word expresses it—to which a bear, cornered and driven to the last extremity, gives utterance—fear, hate, dread, and awful passion mingled and expressed in sound. One can realise the fearful terror which this inspires only when one has, as I have, stood up to a mad bear, repelling charge after charge, with only an iron pike between one's self and those powerful fangs and claws. The long-drawn moan of a polar bear on a frosty night is another phase; this, too, is expressive, but only of those wonderful

Arctic scenes where night and day are as one to this great seal-hunter.

The dog has made man his god,—giving up his life for his master would be but part of his way of showing his love if he had it in his power to do more. So, too, the dog has attempted to adapt his speech to his master's, and the result is a bark. No wild coyotes or wolves bark, but when bands of dogs descended from domesticated animals run wild, their howls are modulated and a certain unmistakable barking quality imparted. The drawnout howl of a great gray wolf is an impressive sound and one never to be forgotten. Only the fox seems to possess the ability to bark in its native tongue. The sounds which the cats, great and small, reproduce are most varied. Nothing can be much more intimidating than the roar of a lion, or more demoniacal than the arguments which our house-pets carry on at night on garden fences.

What use the sounds peculiar to sea-lions subserve in their life on the great ocean, or their haunts along the shore, can only be imagined, but surely such laudable perseverance, day after day, to out-utter each other, must be for some good reason!

Volumes have been written concerning the voices of the two remaining groups of animals— monkeys and birds. In the great family of the four-handed folk, more varieties of sound are produced than would be thought possible. Some of the large baboons are awful in their vocalisations. Terrible agony or remorse is all that their moans suggest to us, no matter what frame of mind on the part of the baboon induces them. Of all vertebrates the tiny marmosets reproduce most exactly the chirps of crickets and similar insects, and to watch one of these little human faces, see its mouth open, and instead of, as seems natural, words issuing forth, to hear these shrill squeaks is most surprising. Young orang-utans, in their "talk," as well as in their actions, are counterparts of human infants. The scream of frantic rage when a banana is offered and jerked away, the wheedling tone when the animal wishes to be comforted by the keeper on account of pain or bruise, and the sound of perfect contentment and happiness when petted by the keeper whom it learns to love,—all are almost indistinguishable from like utterances of a human child.

But how pitiless is the inevitable change of the next few years! Slowly the bones of the cranium thicken, partly filling up the brain cavity, and slowly but surely the ape loses all affection for those who take care of it. More and more morose and sullen it becomes until it reaches a stage of unchangeable ferocity and must be doomed to close confinement, never again to be handled or caressed.

THE NAMES OF ANIMALS, FROGS, AND FISH

WHEN, during the lazy autumn days, the living creatures seem for a time to have taken themselves completely beyond our ken, it may be interesting to delve among old records and descriptions of animals and see how the names by which we know them first came to be given. Many of our English names have an unsuspected ancestry, which, through past centuries, has been handed down to us through many changes of spelling and meaning, of romantic as well as historical interest.

How many people regard the scientific Latin and Greek names of animals with horror, as being absolutely beyond their comprehension, and yet how interesting these names become when we look them squarely in the face, analyse them and find the appropriateness of their application.

When you say "wolf" to a person, the image of that wild creature comes instantly to his mind, but if you ask him *why* it is called a wolf, a hundred chances to one he will look blankly at you. It is the old fault, so common among us human beings, of ignoring the things which lie nearest us. Or perhaps your friend shares the state of mind of the puzzled old lady, who, after looking over a collection of fossil bones, said that she could understand how these bones had been preserved, and millions of years later had been discovered, but it was a mystery to her how anyone could know the names of these ancient animals after such a lapse of time!

Some of the names of the commonest animals are lost in the dimness of antiquity, such as fox, weasel, sheep, dog, and baboon. Of the origin of these we have forever lost the clew. With camel we can go no farther back than the Latin word *camelus,* and elephant balks us with the old Hindoo word *eleph,* which means an ox. The old root of the word wolf meant one who tears or rends, and the application to this animal is obvious. In several English and German names of persons, we have handed down to us a relic of the old fashion of applying wolf as a compliment to a warrior or soldier. For example, Adolph means noble-wolf, and Rudolph glory-wolf.

Lynx is from the same Latin word as the word *lux* (light) and probably was given to these wildcats on account of the brightness of their eyes. Lion is, of course, from the Latin *leo,* which word, in turn, is lost far back in the Egyptian tongue, where the word for the king of beasts was *labu.* The compound word leopard is first found in the Persian language, where *pars* stands for panther. Seal, very appropriately, was once a word meaning "of the sea"; close to the Latin *sal,* the sea.

Many names of animals are adapted from words in the ancient language of the natives in whose country the creatures were first discovered. Puma, jaguar, tapir, and peccary (from *paquires*) are all names from South American Indian languages. The coyote and ocelot were called *coyotl* and *ocelotl* by the Mexicans long before Cortes landed on their shores. Zebra, gorilla, and chimpanzee are native African words, and orang-utan is Malay, meaning Man of the Woods. Cheetah is from some East Indian tongue, as is tahr, the name of the wild goat of the Himalayas. Gnu is from the Hottentots, and giraffe from the Arabic *zaraf*. Aoudad, the Barbary wild sheep, is the French form of the Moorish name *audad*.

The native Indians of our own country are passing rapidly, and before many years their race may be extinct, but their musical, euphonious names of the animals they knew so well, often pleased the ear of the early settlers, and in many instances will be a lasting memorial as long as these forest creatures of our United States survive.

Thus, moose is from the Indian word *mouswah,* meaning wood-eater; skunk from *seganku,* an Algonquin term; *wapiti,* in the Cree language, meant white deer, and was originally applied to the Rocky Mountain goat, but the name is now restricted to the American elk. Caribou is also an Indian word; opossum is from *possowne,* and raccoon is from the Indian *arrathkune* (by further apheresis, coon).

Rhinoceros is pure Greek, meaning nose-horned, but beaver has indeed had a rough time of it in its travels through various languages. It is hardly recognisable as *bebrus, babbru,* and *bbru.* The latter is the ultimate root of our word brown. The original application was, doubtless, on account of the colour of the creature's fur. Otter takes us back to Sanskrit, where we find it *udra.* The significance of this word is in its close kinship to *udan,* meaning water.

The little mouse hands his name down through the years from the old, old Sanskrit, the root meaning to steal. Many people who never heard of Sanskrit have called him and his descendants by terms of homologous significance! The word muscle is from the same root, and was applied from a fancied resemblance of the movement of the muscle beneath the skin to a mouse in motion —not a particularly quieting thought to certain members of the fair sex! The origin of the word rat is less certain, but it may have been derived from the root of the Latin word *radere,* to scratch, or *rodere,* to gnaw. Rodent is derived from the latter term. Cat is also in doubt, but is first recognised in *catalus,* a diminutive of *canis,* a dog. It was applied to the young of almost any animal, as we use the words pup, kitten, cub, and so forth.

Bear is the result of tongue-twisting from the Latin *fera,* a wild beast.

Ape is from the Sanskrit *kapi; kap* in the same language means tremble; but the connection is not clear. Lemur, the name given to that low family of monkeys, is from the plural Latin word *lemures,* meaning ghost or spectre. This has reference to the nocturnal habits, stealthy gait, and weird expression of these large-eyed creatures. Antelope is probably of Grecian origin, and was originally applied to a half-mythical animal, located on the banks of the Euphrates, and described as "very savage and fleet, and having long, saw-like horns with which it could cut down trees. It figures largely in the peculiar fauna of heraldry."

Deer is of obscure origin, but may have been an adjective meaning wild. Elk is derived from the same root as eland, and the history of the latter word is an interesting one. It meant a sufferer, and was applied by the Teutons to the elk of the Old World on account of the awkward gait and stiff movements of this ungainly animal. But in later years the Dutch carried the same word, eland, to South Africa, and there gave it to the largest of the tribe of antelopes, in which sense it is used by zoologists to-day.

Porcupine has arisen from two Latin words, *porcus,* a hog, and *spina,* a spine; hence, appropriately, a spiny-hog. Buffalo may once have

been some native African name. In the vista of
time, our earliest glimpse of it is as *bubalus,*
which was applied both to the wild ox and to a
species of African antelope. Fallow deer is from
fallow, meaning pale, or yellowish, while axis, as
applied to the deer so common in zoological gardens, was first mentioned by Pliny and is doubtless of East Indian origin. The word bison is from
the Anglo-Saxon *wesend,* but beyond Pliny its
ultimate origin eludes all research.

Marmot, through various distortions, looms up
from Latin times as *mus montanus,* literally a
mountain mouse. Badger is from badge, in allusion to the bands of white fur on its forehead.
The verb meaning to badger is derived from the
old cruel sport of baiting badgers with dogs.

Monkey is from the same root as *monna,* a
woman; more especially an old crone, in reference
to the fancied resemblance of the weazened face
of a monkey to that of a withered old woman.
Madam and madonna are other forms of words
from the same root, so wide and sweeping are the
changes in meaning which usage and time can give
to words.

Squirrel has a poetic origin in the Greek language; its original meaning being shadow-tail.
Tiger is far more intricate. The old Persian word
tir meant arrow, while *tighra* signified sharp. The
application to this great animal was in allusion to
the swiftness with which the tiger leaps upon his

prey. The river Tigris, meaning literally the river Arrow, is named thus from the swiftness of its current.

As to the names of reptiles it is, of course, to the Romans that we are chiefly indebted, as in the case of reptile from *reptilus,* meaning creeping; and crocodile from *dilus,* a lizard. Serpent is also from the Latin *serpens,* creeping, and this from the old Sanskrit root, *sarp,* with the same meaning. This application of the idea of creeping is again found in the word snake, which originally came from the Sanskrit *naga.*

Tortoise harks back to the Latin *tortus,* meaning twisted (hence our word tortuous) and came to be applied to these slow creatures because of their twisted legs. In its evolution through many tongues it has suffered numbers of variations; one of these being turtle, which we use to-day to designate the smaller land tortoises. Terrapin and its old forms *terrapene* and *turpin,* on the contrary, originated in the New World, in the language of the American Redskin.

Cobra-de-capello is Portuguese for hooded snake, while python is far older, the same word being used by the Greeks to denote a spirit, demon, or evil-soothsayer. This name was really given to designate any species of large serpent. *Boa* is Latin and was also applied to a large snake, while the importance of the character of size is seen, perhaps, in our words *bos* and *bovine.*

The word viper is interesting; coming directly from the Romans, who wrote it *vipera*. This in turn is a contraction of the feminine form of the adjective *vivipera*, in reference to the habit of these snakes of bringing forth their young alive.

Lizard, through such forms as *lesarde, lezard, lagarto, lacerto,* is from the Latin *lacertus,* a lizard; while closely related is the word alligator by way of *lagarto, aligarto,* to alligator. The prefix may have arisen as a corruption of an article and a noun, as in the modern Spanish *el lagarto,*—a lizard.

Monitor is Latin for one who reminds, these lizards being so called because they are supposed to give warning of the approach of crocodiles. Asp can be carried back to the *aspis* of the Romans, no trace being found in the dim vistas of preceding tongues.

Gecko, the name of certain wall-hunting lizards, is derived from their croaking cry; while iguana is a Spanish name taken from the old native Haytian appellation *biuana*.

Of the word frog we know nothing, although through the medium of many languages it has had as thorough an evolution as in its physical life. We must also admit our ignorance in regard to toad, backward search revealing only *tade, tode, ted, toode,* and *tadie,* the root baffling all study. Polliwog and tadpole are delightfully easy. Old forms of polliwog are *pollywig, polewiggle,* and *pollwiggle*. This last gives us the clew to our spelling—*pollwiggle,* which, reversed and interpreted in a modern way, is wigglehead, a most appropriate name for these lively little black fellows. Tadpole is somewhat similar; toad-pole, or toad's-head, also very apt when we think of these small-bodied larval forms.

Salamander, which is a Greek word of Eastern origin, was applied in the earliest times to a lizard considered to have the power of extinguishing fire. Newt has a strange history; originating in a wrong division of two words, *"an ewte,"* the latter being derived from *eft,* which is far more correct than newt, though in use now in only a few places. Few fishermen have ever thought of the interesting derivation of the names which they know so well. Of course there are a host of fishes named from a fancied resemblance to familiar terrestrial animals or other things; such as the catfish, and those named after the dog, hog, horse, cow, trunk, devil, angel, sun, and moon.

The word fish has passed through many varied forms since it was *piscis* in the old Latin tongue, and the same is true of shark and skate, which in the same language were *carcharus* and *squatus*. Trout was originally *tructa,* which in turn is lost in a very old Greek word, meaning eat or gnaw. Perch harks back to the Latin *perca,* and the Romans had it from the Greeks, among whom it meant spotted. The Romans said *minutus* when they meant small, and nowadays when we speak of any very small fish we say minnow. Alewife in old English was applied to the women, usually very stout dames, who kept alehouses. The corpulency of the fish to which the same term is given explains its derivation.

The pike is so named from the sharp, pointed snout and long, slim body, bringing to mind the old-time weapon of that name; while pickerel means doubly a little pike, the *er* and *el* (as in cock and cockerel) both being diminutives. Smelt was formerly applied to any small fish and comes, perhaps, from the Anglo-Saxon *smeolt*, which meant smooth—the smoothness and slipperiness of the fish suggesting the name.

Salmon comes directly from the Latin *salmo*, a salmon, which literally meant the leaper, from *salire*—to leap. Sturgeon, from the Saxon was *stiriga*, literally a stirrer, from the habit of the fish of stirring up the mud at the bottom of the water. Dace, through its mediæval forms *darce* and *dars*, is from the same root as our word dart, given on account of the swiftness of the fish.

Anchovy is interesting as perhaps from the Basque word *antzua*, meaning dry; hence the dried fish; and mullet is from the Latin *mullus*. Herring is well worth following back to its origin. We know that the most marked habit of fishes of this type is their herding together in great schools or masses or armies. In the very high German *heri* meant an army or host; hence our word harry and, with a suffix, herring.

Hake in Norwegian means hook, and the term hake or hook-fish was given because of the hooked character of the under-jaw. Mackerel comes from *macarellus* and originally the Latin *macula*— spotted, from the dark spots on the body. Roach and ray both come from the Latin *raria,* applied then as in the latter case now to bottom-living sharks.

Flounder comes from the verb, which in turn is derived from flounce, a word which is lost in antiquity. Tarpon (and the form *tarpum*) may be an Indian word; while there is no doubt as to grouper coming from *garrupa,* a native Mexican name. Chubb (a form of cub) meant a chunky mass or lump, referring to the body of the fish. Shad is lost in *sceadda,* Anglo-Saxon for the same fish.

Lamprey and halibut both have histories, which, at first glance, we would never suspect, although the forms have changed but little. The former have a habit of fastening themselves for hours to stones and rocks, by means of their strong, sucking mouths. So the Latin form of the word *lampetra,* or literally lick-rock, is very appropriate. Halibut is equally so. *But* or *bot* in several languages means a certain flounder-like fish, and in olden times this fish was eaten only on holidays (*i.e.*, holy days).   Hence the combination halibut means really holy-flounder.

The meaning of these words and many others are worth knowing, and it is well to be able to answer with other than ignorance the question "What's in a name?"

THE DYING YEAR

WHEN a radical change of habits occurs, as in the sapsucker, deviating so sharply from the ancient principles of its family, many other forms of life about it are influenced, indirectly, but in a most interesting way. In its tippling operations it wastes quantities of sap which exudes from the numerous holes and trickles down the bark of the wounded tree. This proves a veritable feast for the forlorn remnant of wasps and butterflies,—the year's end stragglers whose flower calyces have fallen and given place to swelling seeds.

Swiftly up wind they come on the scent, eager as hounds on the trail, and they drink and drink of the sweets until they become almost incapable of flying. But, after all, the new lease of life is a vain semblance of better things. Their eggs have long since been laid and their mission in life ended, and at the best their existence is but a matter of days.

It is a sad thing this, and sometimes our heart hardens against Nature for the seeming cruelty of it all. Forever and always, year after year, century upon century, the same tale unfolds itself, —the sacrifice of the individual for the good of the race. A hundred drones are tended and reared, all but one to die in vain; a thousand seeds are sown to rot or to sprout and wither; a million little codfish hatch and begin life hopefully, perhaps all to succumb save one; a million million shrimp and pteropods paddle themselves here and there in the ocean, and every one is devoured by fish or swept into the whalebone tangle from which none ever return. And if a lucky one which survives does so because it has some little advantage over its fellows,—some added quality which gives just the opportunity to escape at the critical moment, —then the race will advance to the extent of that trifle and so carry out the precept of evolution. But even though we may owe every character of body and mind to the fulfilment of some such inexorable law in the past, yet the witnessing of the operation brings ever a feeling of cruelty, of injustice somewhere.

How pitiful the weak flight of the last yellow butterfly of the year, as with tattered and battered wings it vainly seeks for a final sip of sweets! The fallen petals and the hard seeds are black and odourless, the drops of sap are hardened. Little by little the wings weaken, the tiny feet clutch convulsively at a dried weed stalk, and the four golden wings drift quietly down among the yellow leaves, soon to merge into the dark mould beneath. As the butterfly dies, a stiffened Katydid scratches a last requiem on his

wing covers—"*katy-didn't—katy-did—kate—y*"
—and the succeeding moment of silence is broken
by the sharp rattle of a woodpecker. We shake
off every dream of the summer and brace ourselves to meet and enjoy the keen, invigorating
pleasures of winter.

NOVEMBER

NOVEMBER'S BIRDS OF THE HEAVENS

AS the whirling winds of winter's edge strip the trees bare of their last leaves, the leaden sky of the eleventh month seems to push its cold face closer to earth. Who can tell when the northern sparrows first arrive? A whirl of brown leaves scatters in front of us; some fall back to earth; others rise and perch in the thick briers,—sombre little white-throated and tree sparrows! These brown-coated, low-voiced birds easily attract our attention, the more now that the great host of brilliant warblers has passed, just as our hearts warm toward the humble poly-pody fronds (passing them by unnoticed when flowers are abundant) which now hold up their bright greenness amid all the cold.

But all the migrants have not left us yet by any means, and we had better leave our boreal visitors until midwinter's blasts show us these hardiest of the hardy at their best.

We know little of the ways of the gaunt herons on their southward journey, but day after day, in the marshes and along the streams, we may see the great blues as they stop in their flight to rest for a time.

The cold draws all the birds of a species together. Dark hordes of clacking grackles pass by, scores of red-winged blackbirds and cowbirds mingle amicably together, both of dark hue but of such unlike matrimonial habits. A single male red-wing, as we have seen, may assume the cares of a harem of three, four, or five females, each of which rears her brown-streaked offspring in her own particular nest, while the valiant guardian keeps faithful watch over his small colony among the reeds and cat-tails. But little thought or care does mother cowbird waste upon her offspring. No home life is hers—merely a stealthy approach to the nest of some unsuspecting yellow warbler, or other small bird, a hastily deposited egg, and the unnatural parent goes on her way, having shouldered all her household cares on another. Her young may be hatched and carefully reared by the patient little warbler mother, or the egg may spoil in the deserted nest, or be left in the cold beneath another nest bottom built over it; little cares the cowbird.

The ospreys or fish hawks seem to circle southward in pairs or trios, but some clear, cold day the sky will be alive with hawks of other kinds. It is a strange fact that these birds which have the power to rise so high that they fairly disappear from our sight choose the trend of terrestrial valleys whenever possible, in directing their aerial routes. Even the series of New Jersey hills, flattered by the name of the Orange Mountains, seem to balk many hawks which elect to change their direction and fly to the right or left toward certain gaps or passes. Through these a raptorial stream pours in such numbers during the period of migration that a person with a fore-knowledge of their path in former years may lie in wait and watch scores upon scores of these birds pass close overhead within a few hours, while a short distance to the right or left one may watch all day without seeing a single raptor. The whims of migrating birds are beyond our ken.

Sometimes, out in the broad fields, one's eyes will be drawn accidentally upward, and a great flight of hawks will be seen—a compact flock of intercircling forms, perhaps two or three hundred in all, the whole number gradually passing from view in a southerly direction, now and then sending down a shrill cry. It is a beautiful sight, not very often to be seen near a city—unless watched for.

To a dweller in a city or its suburbs I heartily commend at this season the forming of this habit, —to look upward as often as possible on your walks. An instant suffices to sweep the whole heavens with your eye, and if the distant circling forms, moving in so stately a manner, yet so swiftly, and in their every movement personifying the essence of wild and glorious freedom,—if this sight does not send a thrill through the onlooker, then he may at once pull his hat lower over his eyes and concern himself only with his immediate business. The joys of Nature are not for such as he; the love of the wild which exists in every one of us is, in him, too thickly "sicklied o'er" with the veneer of convention and civilisation.

Even as late as November, when the water begins to freeze in the tiny cups of the pitcher plants, and the frost brings into being a new kind of foliage on glass and stone, a few insect-eaters of the summer woods still linger on. A belated red-eyed vireo may be chased by a snowbird, and when we approach a flock of birds, mistaking them at a distance for purple finches, we may discover they are myrtle warblers, clad in the faded yellow of their winter plumage. In favoured localities these brave little birds may even spend the entire winter with us.

One of the best of November's surprises may come when all hope of late migrants has been given up. Walking near the river, our glance falls on what might be a painter's palate with blended colours of all shades resting on the smooth surface of the water. We look again and again, hardly believing our eyes, until at last the gorgeous creature takes to wing, and goes humming down the stream, a bit of colour tropical in its extravagance—and we know that we have seen a male wood, or summer, duck in the full grandeur of his white, purple, chestnut, black, blue, and brown. Many other ducks have departed, but this one still swims among the floating leaves on secluded waterways.

Now is the time when the woodcock rises from his swampy summer home and zigzags his way to a land where earthworms are still active. Sometimes in our walks we may find the fresh body of one of these birds, and an upward glance at the roadside will show the cause—the cruel telegraph wires against which the flight of the bird has carried it with fatal velocity.

One of the greatest pleasures which November has to give us is the joy of watching for the long lines of wild geese from the Canada lakes. Who can help being thrilled at the sight of these strong-winged birds, as the V-shaped flock throbs into view high in air, beating over land and water, forest and city, as surely and steadily as the passing of the day behind them. One of the finest of November sounds is the "Honk! honk!" which comes to our ears from such a company of geese, —musical tones "like a clanking chain drawn through the heavy air."

At the stroke of midnight I have been halted in my hurried walk by these notes. They are a bit of the wild north which may even enter within a city, and three years ago I trapped a fine gander and a half a dozen of his flock in the New York Zoological Park, where they have lived ever since and reared their golden-hued goslings, which

otherwise would have broken their shells on some
Arctic waste, with only the snowbirds to admire,
and to be watched with greedy eyes by the Arctic
owls.

> A haze on the far horizon,
>   The infinite tender sky,
> The ripe, rich tints of the cornfields,
>   And the wild geese sailing high;
> And ever on upland and lowland,
>   The charm of the golden-rod—
> Some of us call it Autumn,
>   And others call it God.

W. H. CARRUTH.

A PLEA FOR THE SKUNK

IN spite of constant persecution the skunk is
without doubt the tamest of all of our wild
animals, and shares with the weasel and mink
the honour of being one of the most abundant of
the carnivores, or flesh-eaters, near our homes.
This is a great achievement for the skunk,—to
have thus held its own in the face of ever advancing and destroying civilisation. But the same
characteristics which enable it to hold its ground
are also those which emancipate it from its wild
kindred and give it a unique position among animals. Its first cousins, the minks and weasels,
all secrete pungent odours, which are unpleasant
enough at close range, but in the skunk the great
development of these glands has caused a radical
change in its habits of life and even in its physical
make-up.

Watch a mink creeping on its sinuous way,—
every action and glance full of fierce wildness,
each step telling of insatiable seeking after living, active prey. The boldest rat flees in frantic
terror at the hint of this animal's presence; but
let man show himself, and with a demoniacal grin
of hatred the mink slinks into covert.

Now follow a skunk in its wanderings as it
comes out of its hole in early evening, slowly

stretches and yawns, and with hesitating, rolling gait ambles along, now and then sniffing in the grass and seizing some sluggish grasshopper or cricket. Fearlessness and confidence are what its gait and manner spell. The world is its debtor, and all creatures in its path are left unmolested, only on evidence of good behaviour. Far from need of concealment, its furry coat is striped with a broad band of white, signalling in the dusk or the moonlight, "Give me room to pass and go in peace! Trouble me and beware!"

Degenerate in muscles and vitality, the skunk must forego all strenuous hunts and trust to craft and sudden springs, or else content himself with the humble fare of insects, helpless young birds, and poor, easily confused mice. The flesh of the skunk is said to be sweet and toothsome, but few creatures there are who dare attempt to add it to their bill of fare! A great horned owl or a puma in the extremity of starvation, or a vulture in dire stress of hunger,—probably no others.

Far from wilfully provoking an attack, the skunk is usually content to go on his way peacefully, and when one of these creatures becomes accustomed to the sight of an observer, no more interesting and, indeed, safer object of study can be found.

Depart once from the conventional mode of greeting a skunk,—and instead of hurling a stone in its direction and fleeing, place, if the opportunity present itself, bits of meat in its way evening after evening, and you will soon learn that there is nothing vicious in the heart of the skunk. The evening that the gentle animal appears leading in her train a file of tiny infant skunks, you will feel well repaid for the trouble you have taken. Baby skunks, like their elders, soon learn to know their friends, and are far from being at hair-trigger poise, as is generally supposed.

THE LESSON OF THE WAVE

THE sea and the sky and the shore were at perfect peace on the day when the young gull first launched into the air, and flew outward over the green, smooth ocean. Day after day his parents had brought him fish and squid, until his baby plumage fell from him and his beautiful wing-feathers shot forth,—clean-webbed and elastic. His strong feet had carried him for days over the expanse of sand dunes and pebbles, and now and then he had paddled into deep pools and bathed in the cold salt water. Most creatures of the earth are limited to one or the other of these two elements, but now the gull was proving his mastery over a third. The land, the sea, were left below, and up into the air drifted the beautiful bird, every motion confident with the instinct of ages.

The usefulness of his mother's immaculate breast now becomes apparent. A school of small fish basking near the surface rise and fall with the gentle undulating swell, seeing dimly overhead the blue sky, flecked with hosts of fleecy white clouds. A nearer, swifter cloud approaches, hesitates, splashes into their midst,—and the parent gull has caught her first fish of the day. Instinctively the young bird dives; in his joy of

very life he cries aloud,—the gull-cry which his
ancestors of long ago have handed down to him.
At night he seeks the shore and tucks his bill
into his plumage; and all because of something
within him, compelling him to do these things.

But far from being an automaton, his bright
eye and full-rounded head presage higher things.
Occasionally his mind breaks through the mist of
instinct and reaches upward to higher activity.

As with the other wild kindred of the ocean,
food was the chief object of the day's search.
Fish were delicious, but were not always to be
had; crabs were a treat indeed, when caught unawares, but for mile after mile along the coast
were hosts of mussels and clams,—sweet and
lucious, but incased in an armour of shell, through
which there was no penetrating. However swift
a dash was made upon one of these,—always the
clam closed a little quicker, sending a derisive
shower of drops over the head of the gull.

Once, after a week of rough weather, the storm
gods brought their battling to a climax. Great
green walls of foaming water crashed upon the
rocks, rending huge boulders and sucking them
down into the black depths. Over and through the
spray dashed the gull, answering the wind's howl
—shriek for shriek, poising over the fearful bat-
tlefield of sea and shore.

A wave mightier than all hung and curved, and
a myriad shell-fish were torn from their sheltered

nooks and hurled high in air, to fall broken and helpless among the boulders. The quick eye of the gull saw it all, and at that instant of intensest chaos of the elements, the brain of the bird found itself.

Shortly afterward came night and sleep, but the new-found flash of knowledge was not lost.

The next day the bird walked at low tide into the stronghold of the shell-fish, roughly tore one from the silky strands of its moorings, and carrying it far upward let it fall at random among the rocks. The toothsome morsel was snatched from its crushed shell and a triumphant scream told of success,—a scream which, could it have been interpreted, should have made a myriad, myriad mussels shrink within their shells!

From gull to gull, and from flock to flock, the new habit spread, imitation taking instant advantage of this new source of food. When to-day we walk along the shore and see flocks of gulls playing ducks and drakes with the unfortunate shell-fish, give them not too much credit, but think of some bird which in the long ago first learned the lesson, whether by chance or, as I have suggested, by observing the victims of the waves.

·　　·　　·　　·　　:·　　·　　·:

No scientific facts are these, but merely a logical reasoning deduced from the habits and traits of the birds as we know them to-day; a theory to hold in mind while we watch for its confirmation in the beginning of other new and analogous habits.

> The world is too much with us; late and soon,
>   Getting and spending, we lay waste our powers;
> Little we see in Nature that is ours;
> We have given our hearts away, a sordid boon!
> This sea that bares her bosom to the moon,
>   The winds that will be howling at all hours,
>   And are up-gather'd now like sleeping flowers;
> For this, for everything, we are out of tune;
> It moves us not.—Great God! I'd rather be
>   A Pagan suckled in a creed outworn;
> So might I, standing on this pleasant lea,
>   Have glimpses that would make me less forlorn;
> Have sight of Proteus rising from the sea;
>   Or hear old Triton blow his wreathèd horn.
>
> WILLIAM WORDSWORTH.

WE GO A-SPONGING

WHEN a good compound microscope becomes as common an object in our homes as is a clock or a piano, we may be certain that the succeeding generation will grow up with a much broader view of life and a far greater realisation of the beauties of the natural world. To most of us a glance through a microscope is almost as unusual a sight as the panorama from a balloon. While many of the implements of a scientist arouse enthusiasm only in himself, in the case of the revelations of this instrument, the average person, whatever his profession, cannot fail to be interested.

Many volumes have been written on the microscopic life of ponds and fields, and in a short essay only a hint of the delights of this fascinating study can be given.

Any primer of Natural History will tell us that our bath sponges are the fibrous skeletons of aquatic animals which inhabit tropical seas, but few people know that in the nearest pond there are real sponges, growing sometimes as large as one's head and which are not very dissimilar to those taken from among the corals of the Bahamas. We may bring home a twig covered with a thick growth of this sponge; and by

282

dropping a few grains of carmine into the water, the currents which the little sponge animals set up are plainly visible. In winter these all die, and leave within their meshes numbers of tiny winter buds, which survive the cold weather and in the spring begin to found new colonies. If we examine the sponges in the late fall we may find innumerable of these statoblasts, as they are called.

Scattered among them will sometimes be crowds of little wheels, surrounded with double-ended hooks. These have no motion and we shall probably pass them by as minute burrs or seeds of some water plant. But they, too, are winter buds of a strange group of tiny animals. These are known as Polyzoans or Bryozoans; and though to the eye a large colony of them appears only as a mass of thick jelly, yet when placed in water and left quiet, a wonderful transformation comes over the bit of gelatine. . . . "Perhaps while you gaze at the reddish jelly a pink little projection appears within the field of your lens, and slowly lengthens and broadens, retreating and reappearing, it may be, many times, but finally, after much hesitation, it suddenly seems to burst into bloom. A narrow body, so deeply red that it is often almost crimson, lifts above the jelly a crescentic disc ornamented with two rows of long tentacles that seem as fine as hairs, and they glisten and sparkle like lines of crystal as they wave and float

and twist the delicate threads beneath your
wondering gaze. Then, while you scarcely
breathe, for fear the lovely vision will fade,
another and another spreads its disc and waves its
silvery tentacles, until the whole surface of that
ugly jelly mass blooms like a garden in Paradise
—blooms not with motionless perianths, but with
living animals, the most exquisite that God has
allowed to develop in our sweet waters.'' At the
slightest jar every animal-flower vanishes
instantly.

A wonderful history is behind these little creatures and very different from that of most members of the animal kingdom. While crabs, butterflies, and birds have evolved through many and
varied ancestral forms, the tiny Bryozoans, or,
being interpreted, moss-animals, seem throughout
all past ages to have found a niche for themselves
where strenuous and active competition is absent.
Year after year, century upon century, age upon
age, they have lived and died, almost unchanged
down to the present day. When you look at the
tiny animal, troubling the water and drawing its
inconceivably small bits of food toward it upon
the current made by its tentacles, think of the
earth changes which it has survived.

To the best of our knowledge the Age of Man
is but a paltry fifty thousand years. Behind this
the Age of Mammals may have numbered three
millions; then back of these came the Age of Rep-

tiles with more than seven millions of years, during all of which time the tentacles of unnumbered
generations of Bryozoans waved in the sea. Back,
back farther still we add another seven million
years, or thereabouts, of the Age of the Amphi-
bians, when the coal plants grew, and the Age of
the Fishes. And finally, beyond all exact human
calculation, but estimated at some five million,
we reach the Age of Invertebrates in the Silurian,
and in the lowest of these rocks we find beautifully
preserved fossils of Bryozoans, to all appearances
as perfect in detail of structure as these which we
have before us to-day in this twentieth century
of man's brief reckoning.

These tiny bits of jelly are transfigured as well
by the grandeur of their unchanged lineage as by
the appearance of the little animals from within.
What heraldry can commemorate the beginning
of their race over twenty millions of years in the
past!

The student of mythology will feel at home
when identifying some of the commonest objects
of the pond. And most are well named, too, as
for instance the Hydra, a small tube-shaped creature with a row of active tentacles at one end.
Death seems far from this organism, which is
closely related to the sea-anemones and corals,
for though a very brief drying will serve to kill
it, yet it can be sliced and cut as finely as possible
and each bit, true to its name, will at once proceed

to grow a new head and tentacles complete, becoming a perfect animal.

Then we shall often come across a queer creature with two oar-like feelers near the head and a double tail tipped with long hairs, while in the centre of the head is a large, shining eye,— Cyclops he is rightly called. Although so small that we can make out little of his structure without the aid of the lens, yet Cyclops is far from being related to the other still smaller beings which swim about him, many of which consist of but one cell and are popularly known as animalculæ, more correctly as Protozoans. Cyclops has a jointed body and in many other ways shows his relationship to crabs and lobsters, even though they are many times larger and live in salt water.

Another member of this group is Daphnia, although the appropriateness of this name yet remains to be discovered; Daphnia being a chunky-bodied little being, with a double-branched pair of oar-like appendages, with which he darts swiftly through the water. Although covered with a hard crust like a crab, this is so transparent that we can see right through his body. The dark mass of food in the stomach and the beating heart are perfectly distinct. Often, near the upper part of the body, several large eggs are seen in a sort of pouch, where they are kept until hatched.

So if the sea is far away and time hangs heavy, invite your friends to go sponging and crabbing in the nearest pond, and you may be certain of quieting their fears as to your sanity as well as drawing exclamations of delight from them when they see these beautiful creatures for the first time.

DECEMBER

NEW THOUGHTS ABOUT NESTS

OUR sense of smell is not so keen as that of a dog, who can detect the tiny quail while they are still invisible; nor have we the piercing sight of the eagle who spies the grouse crouching hundreds of feet beneath his circling flight; but when we walk through the bare December woods there is unfolded at last to our eyes evidence of the late presence of our summer's feathered friends—air castles and tree castles of varied patterns and delicate workmanship.

Did it ever occur to you to think what the first nest was like—what home the first reptile-like scale flutterers chose? Far back before Jurassic times, millions of years ago, before the coming of bony fishes, when the only mammals were tiny nameless creatures, hardly larger than mice; when the great Altantosaurus dinosaurs browsed on the quaint herbage, and Pterodactyls—those ravenous bat-winged dragons of the air—hovered above the surface of the earth,—in this epoch we can imagine a pair of long-tailed, half-winged creatures which skimmed from tree to tree, perhaps giving an occasional flop—the beginning of the marvellous flight motions. Is it not likely that the Teleosaurs who watched hungrily from the swamps saw them disappear at last in a hollowed cavity beneath a rotten knothole? Here. perhaps, the soft-shelled, lizard-like eggs were laid, and when they gave forth the ugly creaturelings did not Father Creature flop to the topmost branch and utter a gurgling cough, a most unpleasant grating sound, but grand in its significance, as the opening chord in the symphony of the ages to follow?—until now the mockingbird and the nightingale hold us spellbound by the wonder of their minstrelsy.

Turning from our imaginary picture of the ancient days, we find that some of the birds of the present time have found a primitive way of nesting still the best. If we push over this rotten stump we shall find that the cavity near the top, where the wood is still sound, has been used the past summer by the downy woodpecker—a front door like an auger hole, ceiling of rough-hewn wood, a bed of chips!

The chickadee goes a step further, and shows his cleverness in sometimes choosing a cavity already made, and instead of rough, bare chips, the six or eight chickadee youngsters are happy on a hair mattress of a closely woven felt-like substance.

Perhaps we should consider the kingfisher the most barbarous of all the birds which form a shelter for their home. With bill for pick and shovel, she bores straight into a sheer clay bank, and at the end of a six-foot tunnel her young are reared, their nest a mass of fish bones—the residue of their dinners. Then there are the aerial masons and brickmakers—the eave swallows, who carry earth up into the air, bit by bit, and attach it to the eaves, forming it into a globular, long-necked flask. The barn swallows mix the clay with straw and feathers and so form very firm structures on the rafters above the haymows.

But what of the many nests of grasses and twigs which we find in the woods? How closely they were concealed while the leaves were on the trees, and how firm and strong they were while in use, the strongest wind and rain of summer only rocking them to and fro! But now we must waste no time or they will disappear. In a month or more almost all will have dissolved into fragments and fallen to earth—their mission accomplished.

Some look as if disintegration had already begun, but if we had discovered them earlier in the year, we should have seen that they were never less fragile or loosely constructed than we find them now. Such is a cuckoo's nest, such a mourning dove's or a heron's; merely a flat platform of a few interlaced twigs, through which the eggs are visible from below. Why, we ask, are some birds so careless or so unskilful? The European cuckoo, like our cowbird, is a parasite, laying her eggs in the nests of other birds; so, perhaps, neglect of household duties is in the blood. But this style of architecture seems to answer all the requirements of doves and herons, and, although with one sweep of the hand we can demolish one of these flimsy platforms, yet such a nest seems somehow to resist wind and rain just as long as the bird needs it.

Did you ever try to make a nest yourself? If not, sometime take apart a discarded nest—even the simplest in structure—and try to put it together again. Use no string or cord, but fasten it to a crotch, put some marbles in it and visit it after the first storm. After you have picked up all the marbles from the ground you will appreciate more highly the skill which a bird shows in the construction of its home. Whether a bird excavates its nest in earth or wood, or weaves or plasters it, the work is all done by means of two straight pieces of horn—the bill.

There is, however, one useful substance which aids the bird—the saliva which is formed in the mucous glands of the mouth. Of course the first and natural function of this fluid is to soften the food before it passes into the crop; but in those birds which make their nests by weaving together pieces of twig, it must be of great assistance in softening the wood and thus enabling the bird readily to bend the twigs into any required position. Thus the catbird and rose-breasted grosbeak weave.

Given a hundred or more pieces of twigs, each

an inch in length, even a bird would make but little progress in forming a cup-shaped nest, were it not that the sticky saliva provided cement strong and ready at hand. So the chimney swift finds no difficulty in forming and attaching her mosaic of twigs to a chimney, using only very short twigs which she breaks off with her feet while she is on the wing.

How wonderfully varied are the ways which birds adopt to conceal their nests. Some avoid suspicion by their audacity, building near a frequented path, in a spot which they would never be suspected of choosing. The hummingbird studs the outside of its nest with lichens, and the vireo drapes a cobweb curtain around her fairy cup. Few nests are more beautiful and at the same time more durable than a vireo's. I have seen the nests of three successive years in the same tree, all built, no doubt, by the same pair of birds, the nest of the past summer perfect in shape and quality, that of the preceding year threadbare, while the home which sheltered the brood of three summers ago is a mere flattened skeleton, reminding one of the ribs and stern post of a wrecked boat long pounded by the waves.

The subject of nests has been sadly neglected by naturalists, most of whom have been chiefly interested in the owners or the contents; but when the whys and wherefores of the homes of birds are made plain we shall know far more concerning the little carpenters, weavers, masons, and basket-makers who hang our groves and decorate our shrubbery with their skill. When on our winter's walk we see a distorted, wind-torn, grass cup, think of the quartet of beautiful little creatures, now flying beneath some tropical sun, which owe their lives to the nest, and which, if they are spared, will surely return to the vicinity next summer.

> That time of year thou may'st in me behold,
> When yellow leaves, or none, or few, do hang
> Upon those boughs which shake against the cold,—
> Bare, ruin'd choirs, where late the sweet birds sang.
>
> SHAKESPEARE.

LESSONS FROM AN ENGLISH SPARROW

MANY people say they love Nature, but as they have little time to go into the country they have to depend on books for most of their information concerning birds, flowers, and other forms of life. There is, however, no reason why one should not, even in the heart of a great city, begin to cultivate his powers of observation. Let us take, for example, the omnipresent English sparrow. Most of us probably know the difference between the male and female English sparrows, but I venture to say that not one in ten persons could give a satisfactory description of the colours of either. How much we look and how little we really see!

Little can be said in favour of the English sparrows' disposition, but let us not blame them for their unfortunate increase in numbers. Man brought them from England, where they are kept in check by Nature's wise laws. These birds were deliberately introduced where Nature was not prepared for them.

When we put aside prejudice we can see that the male bird, especially when in his bright spring colours, is really very attractive, with his ashy gray head, his back streaked with black and bay, the white bar on his wings and the jet black chin

and throat contrasting strongly with the uniformly light-coloured under parts. If this were
a rare bird the "black-throated sparrow" would
enjoy his share of admiration.

It is wonderful how he can adapt himself to new
conditions, nesting anywhere and everywhere, and
this very adaptation is a sign of a very high order
of intelligence. He has, however, many characteristics which tell us of his former life. A few of
the habits of this bird may be misleading. His
thick, conical bill is made for crushing seeds, but
he now feeds on so many different substances that
its original use, as shown by its shape, is obscured.
If there were such a thing as vaudeville among
birds, the common sparrow would be a star imita-
tor. He clings to the bark of trees and picks out
grubs, supporting himself with his tail like a
woodpecker; he launches out into the air, taking
insects on the wing like a flycatcher; he clings like
a chickadee to the under side of twigs, or hovers
in front of a heap of insect eggs, presenting a
feeble imitation of a hummingbird. These modes
of feeding represent many different families of
birds.

Although his straw and feather nests are shape-
less affairs, and he often feeds on garbage, all
æsthetic feeling is not lost, as we see when he
swells out his black throat and white cravat,
spreads tail and wing and beseeches his lady-love
to admire him. Thus he woos her as long as he

is alone, but when several other eager suitors
arrive, his patience gives out, and the courting
turns into a football game. Rough and tumble is
the word, but somehow in the midst of it all, her
highness manages to make her mind known and
off she flies with the lucky one. Thus we have
represented, in the English sparrows, the two extremes of courtship among birds.

It is worth noting that the male alone is ornamented, the colours of the female being much
plainer. This dates from a time when it was
necessary for the female to be concealed while
sitting on the eggs. The young of both sexes are
coloured like their mother, the young males not
acquiring the black gorget until perfectly able to
take care of themselves. About the plumage there
are some interesting facts. The young bird moults
twice before the first winter. The second moult
brings out the mark on the throat, but it is rusty
now, not black in colour; his cravat is grayish and
the wing bar ashy. In the spring, however, a
noticeable change takes place, but neither by the
moulting nor the coming in of plumage. The
shaded edges of the feathers become brittle and
break off, bringing out the true colours and making them clear and brilliant. The waistcoat is
brushed until it is black and glossy, the cravat
becomes immaculate, and the wristband or wing
bar clears up until it is pure white.

The homes of these sparrows are generally composed of a great mass of straw and feathers, with the nest in the centre; but the spotted eggs, perhaps, show that these birds once built open nests, the dots and marks on the eggs being of use in concealing their conspicuous white ground. Something seems already to have hinted to Nature that this protection is no longer necessary, and we often find eggs almost white, like those of woodpeckers and owls, which nest in dark places.

We have all heard of birds flocking together for some mutual benefit—the crows, for instance, which travel every winter day across country to favourite "roosts." In the heart of a city we can often study this same phenomenon of birds gathering together in great flocks. In New York City, on One Hundred and Twenty-fifth Street, there stands a tree—a solitary reminder of the forest which once covered all this paved land. To this, all winter long, the sparrows begin to flock about four or five o'clock in the afternoon. They come singly and in twos and threes until the bare limbs are black with them and there seems not room for another bird; but still they come, each new arrival diving into the mass of birds and causing a local commotion. By seven o'clock there are hundreds of English sparrows perching in this one tree. At daylight they are off again, whirring away by scores, and in a few minutes the tree is silent and empty. The same habit is to be seen in many other cities and towns, for thus the birds gain mutual warmth.

Nature will do her best to diminish the number of sparrows and to regain the balance, but to do this the sparrow must be brought face to face with as many dangers as our wild birds, and although, owing to the sparrows' fearlessness of man, this may never happen, yet at least the colour protections and other former safeguards are slowly being eliminated. On almost every street we may see albino or partly albino birds, such as those with white tails or wings. White birds exist in a wild state only from some adaptation to their surroundings. A bird which is white simply because its need of protection has temporarily ceased, would become the prey of the first stray hawk which crossed its path. We cannot hope to exterminate the English sparrow even by the most wholesale slaughter, but if some species of small hawk or butcher bird could ever become as fearless an inhabitant of our cities as these birds, their reduction to reasonable numbers would be a matter of only a few months.

> So dainty in plumage and hue,
>   A study in gray and brown,
> How little, how little we knew
>   The pest he would prove to the town!
>
> From dawn until daylight grows dim,
>   Perpetual chatter and scold.
> No winter migration for him,
>   Not even afraid of the cold!

Scarce a song-bird he fails to molest,
Belligerent, meddlesome thing!
Wherever he goes as a guest
He is sure to remain as a King.

MARY ISABELLA FORSYTH.

THE PERSONALITY OF TREES

HOW many of us think of trees almost as we do of the rocks and stones about us,—as all but inanimate objects, standing in the same relation to our earth as does the furry covering of an animal to its owner. The simile might be carried out more in detail, the forests protecting the continents from drought and flood, even as the coat of fur protects its owner from extremes of heat and cold.

When we come to consider the tree as a living individual, a form of life contemporaneous with our own, and to realise that it has its birth and death, its struggles for life and its periods of peace and abundance, we will soon feel for it a keener sympathy and interest and withal a veneration greater than it has ever aroused in us before.

Of all living things on earth, a tree binds us most closely to the past. Some of the giant tortoises of the Galapagos Islands are thought to be four hundred years old and are probably the oldest animals on the earth. There is, however, nothing to compare with the majesty and grandeur of the Sequoias—the giant redwoods of California—the largest of which, still living, reach upward more than one hundred yards above the ground, and show, by the number of their rings, that their life began from three to five thousand years ago. Our deepest feelings of reverence are aroused when we look at a tree which was "one thousand years old when Homer wrote the Iliad; fifteen hundred years of age when Aristotle was foreshadowing his evolution theory and writing his history of animals; two thousand years of age when Christ walked upon earth; nearly four thousand years of age when the 'Origin of Species' was written. Thus the life of one of these trees spanned the whole period before the birth of Aristotle (384 B.C.) and after the death of Darwin (A.D. 1882), the two greatest natural philosophers who have lived."

Considered not only individually, but taken as a group, the Sequoias are among the oldest of the old. Geologically speaking, most of the forms of life now in existence are of recent origin, but a full ten million of years ago these giant trees were developed almost as highly as they are to-day. At the end of the coal period, when the birds and mammals of to-day were as yet unevolved, existing only potentially in the scaly, reptile-like creatures of those days, the Sequoias waved their needles high in air.

In those days these great trees were found over the whole of Canada, Greenland, and Siberia, but the relentless onslaught of the Ice Age wrought terrible destruction and, like the giant tortoises among reptiles, the apteryx among birds, and the bison among mammals, the forlorn hope of the great redwoods, making a last stand in a few small groves of California, awaits total extinction at the hands of the most terrible of Nature's enemies—man. When the last venerable giant trunk has fallen, the last axe-stroke which severs the circle of vital sap will cut the only thread of individual life which joins in time the beating of our pulses to-day with the beginning of human history and philosophy,—thousands of years in the past.

Through all the millions of years during which the evolution of modern forms of life has been going on, then as now, trees must have entered prominently into the environment and lives of the terrestrial animals. Ages ago, long before snakes and four-toed horses were even foreshadowed, and before the first bird-like creatures had appeared, winged reptile-dragons flew about, doubtless roosting or perching on the Triassic and Jurassic trees. Perhaps the very pieces of coal which are burned in our furnaces once bent and swayed under the weight of these bulky animals. Something like six millions of years ago, long-tailed, fluttering birds appeared, with lizard-like claws at the bend of their wings and with jaws filled with teeth. These creatures were certainly arboreal, spending most of their time among the branches of trees. So large were certain great sloth-like creatures that they uprooted the trees bodily, in order to feed on their succulent leaves, sometimes bending their trunks down until their branches were within reach.

On a walk through the woods and fields to-day, how seldom do we find a dead insect! When sick and dying, nine out of ten are snapped up by frog, lizard, or bird; the few which die a natural death seeming to disintegrate into mould within a very short space of time. There is, however, one way in which, through the long, long thousands of centuries, insects have been preserved. The spicy resin which flowed from the ancient pines attracted hosts of insects, which, tempted by their hope of food, met their death—caught and slowly but surely enclosed by the viscid sap, each antenna and hair as perfect as when the insect was alive. Thus, in this strangely fortunate way, we may know and study the insects which, millions of years ago, fed on the flowers or bored into the bark of trees. We have found no way to improve on Nature in this respect, for to-day when we desire to mount a specimen permanently for microscopical work, we imbed it in Canada balsam.

If suddenly the earth should be bereft of all trees, there would indeed be consternation and despair among many classes of animals. Although in the sea there are thousands of creatures, which, by their manner of life, are prohibited from ever passing the boundary line between land and water, yet many sea-worms, as for example the teredo, or ship-worm, are especially fashioned for living in and perhaps feeding on wood, in the shape of stray floating trees and branches, the bottoms of ships, and piles of wharves. Of course the two latter are supplied by man, but even before his time, floating trees at sea must have been plentiful enough to supply homes for the whole tribe of these creatures, unless they made their burrows in coral or shells.

The insects whose very existence, in some cases, depends upon trees, are innumerable. What, for example, would become of the larvæ of the cicada, or locust, which, in the cold and darkness of their subterranean life, for seventeen years suck the juicy roots of trees; or the caterpillars of the moths, spinning high their webs among the leaves; or the countless beetles whose grubs bore through and through the trunk their sinuous, sawdusty tunnels; or the ichneumon fly, which with an instrument—surgical needle, file, augur, and scroll saw all in one—deposits, deep below the bark, its eggs in safety? If forced to compete with terrestrial species, the tree spiders and scorpions would quickly become exterminated; while especially adapted arboreal ants would instantly disappear.

We cannot entirely exclude even fishes from our list; as the absence of mangroves would incidentally affect the climbing perch and catfishes!

The newts and common toads would be in no wise dismayed by the passing of the trees, but not so certain tadpoles. Those of our ditches, it is true, would live and flourish, but there are, in the world, many curious kinds which hatch and grow up into frogs in curled-up leaves or in damp places in the forks of branches, and which would find themselves homeless without trees. Think, too, of the poor green and brown tree frogs with their sucker feet, compelled always to hop along the ground!

Lizards, from tiny swifts to sixty-inch iguanas, would sorely miss the trees, while the lithe green tree snakes and the tree boas would have to change all their life habits in order to be able to exist. But as for the cold, uncanny turtles and alligators,—what are trees to them!

In the evolution of the birds and other animals, the cry of "excelsior" has been followed literally as well as theoretically and, with a few exceptions, the highest in each class have not only risen above their fellows in intelligence and structure, but have left the earth and climbed or flown to the tree-tops, making these their chief place of abode.

Many of the birds which find their food at sea, or in the waters of stream and lake, repair to the trees for the purpose of building their nests among the branches. Such birds are the pelicans, herons, ibises, and ospreys; while the wood ducks lay their eggs high above the ground in the hollows of trees. Parrots, kingfishers, swifts, and hummingbirds are almost helpless on the ground, their feet being adapted for climbing about the branches, perching on twigs, or clinging to the hollows of trees. Taken as a whole, birds would suffer more than any other class of creatures in a deforested world. The woodpeckers would be without home, food, and resting-place; except, possibly, the flicker, or high-hole, who is either a retrograde or a genius, whichever we may choose to consider him, and could live well enough upon ground ants. But as to his nest—he would have to sharpen his wits still more to solve successfully the question of the woodpecker motto, "What is home without a hollow tree?"

Great gaps would be made in the ranks of the furry creatures—the mammals. Opossums and raccoons would find themselves in an embarrassing position, and as for the sloths, which never descend to earth, depending for protection on their resemblance to leaves and mossy bark, they would be wiped out with one fell swoop. The arboreal squirrels might learn to burrow, as so many of their near relations have done, but their muscles would become cramped from inactivity and their eyes would often strain upward for a glimpse of the beloved branches. The bats might take to caves and the vampires to outhouses and dark crevices in the rocks, but most of the monkeys and apes would soon become extinct, while a chimpanzee or orang-utan would become a cripple, swinging ever painfully along between the knuckles of crutch-like forearms, searching, searching forever for the trees which gave him his form and structure, and without which his life and that of his race must abruptly end.

Leaving the relations which trees hold to the animals about them and the part which they have played in the evolution of life on the earth in past epochs, let us consider some of the more humble trees about us. Not, however, from the standpoint of the technical botanist or the scientific forester, but from the sympathetic point of view of a living fellow form, sharing the same planet, both owing their lives to the same great source of all light and heat, and subject to the same extremes of heat and cold, storm and drought. How wonderful, when we come to think of it, is a tree, to be able to withstand its enemies, elemental and animate, year after year, decade after decade, although fast-rooted to one patch of earth. An animal flees to shelter at the approach of gale or cyclone, or travels far in search of abundant food. Like the giant algæ, ever waving upward from the bed of the sea, which depend on the nourishment of the surrounding waters, so the tree blindly trusts to Nature to minister to its needs, filling its leaves with the light-given greenness, and feeling for nutritious salts with the sensitive tips of its innumerable rootlets.

Darwin has taught us, and truly, that a relentless struggle for existence is ever going on around us, and although this is most evident to our eyes in a terrible death battle between two great beasts of prey, yet it is no less real and intense in the case of the bird pouring forth a beautiful song, or the delicate violet shedding abroad its perfume. To realise the host of enemies ever shadowing the feathered songster and its kind, we have only to remember that though four young birds may be hatched in each of fifty nests, yet of the two hundred nestlings an average often of but one lives to grow to maturity,—to migrate and to return to the region of its birth.

And the violet, living, apparently, such a quiet life of humble sweetness? Fortunate indeed is it if its tiny treasure of seeds is fertilized, and then the chances are a thousand to one that they will grow and ripen only to fall by the wayside, or on barren ground, or among the tares.

At first thought, a tree seems far removed from all such struggles. How solemn and grand its trunk stands, column-like against the sky! How puny and weak we seem beside it! Its sturdy roots, sound wood, and pliant branches all spell power. Nevertheless, the old, old struggle is as fierce, as unending, here as everywhere. A monarch of the forest has gained its supremacy only by a lifelong battle with its own kind and with a horde of alien enemies.

From the heart of the tropics to the limit of tree-growth in the northland we find the battle of life waged fiercely, root contending with root for earth-food, branch with branch for the light which means life.

In a severe wrestling match, the moments of supremest strain are those when the opponents are fast-locked, motionless, when the advantage comes, not with quickness, but with staying power; and likewise in the struggle of tree with tree the fact that one or two years, or even whole decades, watch the efforts of the branches to lift their leaves one above the other, detracts nothing from the bitterness of the strife.

Far to the north we will sometimes find groves of young balsam firs or spruce,—hundreds of the same species of sapling growing so close together that a rabbit may not pass between. The slender trunks, almost touching each other, are bare of branches. Only at the top is there light and air, and the race is ever upward. One year some slight advantage may come to one young tree,—some delicate unbalancing of the scales of life, and that fortunate individual instantly responds, reaching several slender side branches over the heads of his brethren. They as quickly show the effects of the lessened light and forthwith the race is at an end. The victor shoots up tall and straight, stamping and choking out the lives at his side, as surely as if his weapons were teeth and claws instead of delicate root-fibres and soughing foliage.

The contest with its fellows is only the first of many. The same elements which help to give it being and life are ever ready to catch it unawares, to rend it limb from limb, or by patient, long-continued attack bring it crashing to the very dust from which sprang the seed.

We see a mighty spruce whose black leafage has waved above its fellows for a century or more, paying for its supremacy by the distortion of every branch. Such are to be seen clinging to the rocky shores of Fundy, every branch and twig curved toward the land; showing the years of battling with constant gales and blizzards. Like giant weather-vanes they stand, and, though there is no elasticity in their limbs and they are gnarled and scarred, yet our hearts warm in admiration of their decades of patient watching beside the troubled waters. For years to come they will defy every blast the storm god can send against them, until, one wild day, when the soil has grown scanty around the roots of one of the weakest, it will shiver and tremble at some terrific onslaught of wind and sleet; it will fold its branches closer about it and, like the Indian chieftains, who perhaps in years past occasionally watched the waters by the side of the young sapling, the conquered tree will bow its head for the last time to the storm.

Farther inland, sheltered in a narrow valley, stands a sister tree, seeded from the same cone as the storm-distorted spruce. The wind shrieks and howls above the little valley and cannot enter; but the law of compensation brings to bear another element, silent, gentle, but as deadly as the howling blast of the gale. All through the long winter the snow sifts softly down, finding easy lodgment on the dense-foliaged branches. From the surrounding heights the white crystals pour down until the tree groans with the massive weight. Her sister above is battling with the storm, but hardly a feather's weight of snow clings to her waving limbs.

The compressed, down-bent branches of the valley spruce soon become permanently bent and the strain on the trunk fibres is great. At last, with a despairing crash, one great limb gives way and is torn bodily from its place of growth. The very vitals of the tree are exposed and instantly every splintered cell is filled with the sifting snow. Helpless the tree stands, and early in the spring, at the first quickening of summer's growth, a salve of curative resin is poured upon the wound. But it is too late. The invading water has done its work and the elements have begun to rot the very heart of the tree. How much more to be desired is the manner of life and death of the first spruce, battling to the very last!

A beech seedling which takes root close to the bank of a stream has a good chance of surviving, since there will be no competitors on the water side and moisture and air will never fail. But look at some ancient beech growing thus, whose smooth, whitened bole encloses a century of growth rings. Offsetting its advantages, the stream, little by little, has undermined the maze of roots and the force of annual freshets has trained them all in a down-stream direction. It is an inverted reminder of the wind-moulded spruce. Although the stout beech props itself by great roots thrown landward, yet, sooner or later, the ripples will filter in beyond the centre of gravity and the mighty tree will topple and mingle with its shadow-double which for so many years the stream has reflected.

Thus we find that while without moisture no tree could exist, yet the same element often brings death. The amphibious mangroves which fringe the coral islands of the southern seas hardly attain to the dignity of trees, but in the mysterious depths of our southern swamps we find the strangely picturesque cypresses, which defy the waters about them. One cannot say where trunk ends and root begins, but up from the stagnant slime rise great arched buttresses, so that the tree seems to be supported on giant six- or eight-legged stools, between the arches of which the water flows and finds no chance to use its power. Here, in these lonely solitudes,—heron-haunted, snake-infested,—the hanging moss and orchids search out every dead limb and cover it with an unnatural greenness. Here, great lichens grow and a myriad tropical insects bore and tunnel their way from bark to heart of tree and back again. Here, in the blackness of night, when the air is heavy with hot, swampy odours, and only the occasional squawk of a heron or cry of some animal is heard, a rending, grinding, crashing, breaks suddenly upon the stillness, a distant boom and splash, awakening every creature. Then tho silence again closes down and we know that a cypress, perhaps linking a trio of centuries, has yielded up its life.

Leaving the hundred other mysteries which the trees of the tropics might unfold, let us consider for a moment the danger which the tall, successful tree invites,—the penalty which it pays for having surpassed all its other brethren. It pre-eminently attracts the bolts of Jove and the lesser trees see a blinding flash, hear a rending of heart wood, and when the storm has passed, the tree, before perfect in trunk, limbs, and foliage, is now but a heap of charred splinters.

Many a great willow overhanging the banks of a wide river could tell interesting tales of the scars on its trunk. That lower wound was a deep gash cut by some Indian, perhaps to direct a war-party making their way through the untrodden wilderness; this bare, unsightly patch was burnt out by the signal fire of one of our forefather pioneers. And so on and on the story would unfold, until the topmost, freshly sawed-off limb had for its purpose only the desire of the present owner for a clearer view of the water beyond.

Finally we come to the tree best beloved of us in the north,—the carefully grafted descendant of some sour little wild crab-apple. A faithful servant indeed has the monarch of the old orchard proved. It has fed us and our fathers before us, and its gnarled trunk and low-hanging branches tell the story of the rosy fruit which has weighed down its limbs year after year. Old age has laid a heavy hand upon it, but not until the outermost twig has ceased to blossom, and its death, unlike that of its wild kindred, has come silently and peacefully, do we give the order to have the tree felled. Even in its death it serves us, giving back from the open hearth the light and heat which it has stored up throughout the summers of many years.

Let us give more thought to the trees about us, and when possible succour them in distress, straighten the bent sapling, remove the parasitic lichen, and give them the best chance for a long, patient, strong life.

In the far North stands a Pine-tree, lone,
  Upon a wintry height;
It sleeps; around it snows have thrown
  A covering of white.

It dreams forever of a Palm
  That, far i' the morning-land,
Stands silent in a most sad calm
  Midst of the burning sand.
    (*From the German of Heine.*) SIDNEY LANIER.

AN OWL OF THE NORTH

IT is midwinter, and from the northland a blizzard of icy winds and swirling snow crystals is sweeping with fury southward over woods and fields. We sit in our warm room before the crackling log fire and listen to the shriek of the gale and wonder how it fares with the little bundles of feathers huddled among the cedar branches.

We picture to ourselves all the wild kindred sheltered from the raging storm; the gray squirrels rocking in their lofty nests of leaves; the chipmunks snug underground; the screech owls deep in the hollow apple trees, all warm and dry.

But there are those for whom the blizzard has no terrors. Far to the north on the barren wastes of Labrador, where the gale first comes in from the sea and gathers strength as it comes, a great owl flaps upward and on broad pinions, white as the driving snowflakes, sweeps southward with the storm. Now over ice-bound river or lake, or rushing past a myriad dark spires of spruce, then hovering wonderingly over a multitude of lights from the streets of some town, the strong Arctic bird forges southward, until one night, if we only knew, we might open our window and, looking upward, see two great yellow eyes apparently hanging in space, the body and wings of the bird in snow-white plumage lost amidst the flakes. We thrill in admiration at the grand bird, so fearless of the raging elements.

Only the coldest and fiercest storms will tempt him from the north, and then not because he fears snow or cold, but in order to keep within reach of the snowbirds which form his food. He seeks for places where a less severe cold encourages small birds to be abroad, or where the snow's crust is less icy, through which the field mice may bore their tunnels, and run hither and thither in the moonlight, pulling down the weeds and cracking their frames of ice. Heedless of passing clouds, these little rodents scamper about, until a darker, swifter shadow passes, and the feathered talons of the snowy owl close over the tiny, shivering bundle of fur.

Occasionally after such a storm, one may come across this white owl in some snowy field, hunting in broad daylight; and that must go down as a red-letter day, to be remembered for years.

What would one not give to know of his adventures since he left the far north. What stories he could tell of hunts for the ptarmigan,—those Arctic fowl, clad in plumage as white as his own; or the little kit foxes, or the seals and polar bears playing the great game of life and death among the grinding icebergs!

His visit to us is a short one. Comes the first hint of a thaw and he has vanished like a melting snowflake, back to his home and his mate. There in a hollow in the half-frozen Iceland moss, in February, as many as ten fuzzy little snowy owlets may grow up in one nest,—all as hardy and beautiful and brave as their great fierce-eyed parents.

THE END